Re[vised Edition]

Glam[our Doll]s

of the 1950s & 1960s

Identification & Values

by Polly & Pam Judd

Alexander *Pamela* (see page 43).

Published by Hobby House Press

Cumberland, Maryland 21502

DEDICATION

This book is dedicated to our family, Wally Sr., Wally Jr., Donna, Eryn and Kyle.

ACKNOWLEDGEMENTS

There have been many people who have helped the authors in the completion of this book. We would like to take this opportunity to acknowledge and thank them for their help.

There were many individuals who helped in various sections of the book. Susan Manos and Sandy Goss helped in many ways with the *Barbie*® section. Marianne Gardner was always available to help with the Alexander section. Sharlene Doyle shared knowledge and photographs. Inga Tomoletz was always on the lookout for unusual dolls. Mary Elizabeth Poole shared her longtime research with us. Laura May Brown was always ready to search for and photograph dolls on the East Coast. Dorothy Hesner aided us with her wonderful letters from Chicago and her knowledge from her past experience.

We are honored to have photographs of dolls from California, Colorado, Florida, Illinois, Maryland, Michigan, New York, North Carolina, Ohio, Oregon, Pennsylvania, Tennessee and Virginia. We are delighted to have a German *Lilli*® doll from Stefanie Deutsch of West Germany.

There were many people who permitted us to use their dolls in photographs or helped us in other ways. They include: Joyce M. Alderson, Barbara Andresen, Sherry Baloun, Peggy Bealferd, Ester Borgis, Patricia Dycus Callender, Beatrice F. Campbell, Barbara Comienski, Ann M. Condron, Carole Correll, Sherri L. Dempsey, Patricia Driggs, Maureen Edick, Gayle Elam, Pat Freeman, Marianne Gardner, Kathy George, Jean Hall, Dolly Jakubecz, Eryn Judd, Donald Kallan, M. Catherine Lawrence, Christine Lorman, Marybeth Manchook, Marge Meisinger, Susan Miller, Peggie Murray, Jacki O'Connor, Phyllis Parr, Lisa Patrick, Pat Parton, Anne Pendleton, Thelma Purvis, Eleanor Quednau, Nancy Roeder, Lanell Rowland, Louise Schnell, Suzanne Schroeder, Lois Seketa, Betty Shriver, Evelyn M. Smith, Sandra Strater, Pat Timmons, Trudy Vasiloff and Gigi Williams.

We are grateful to our editor, Donna Felger, and the entire staff of Hobby House Press, Inc.

Barbie® is a registered trademark of Mattel, Inc.
Lilli® is a registered trademark of Bild Lilli.

Additional Copies of this book may be purchased at $12.95
from
HOBBY HOUSE PRESS, INC.
Cumberland, Maryland 21502
1-800-554-1447
or from your favorite bookstore or dealer.
Please add $4.75 per copy postage.

ISBN: 0-87588-410-5

TABLE OF CONTENTS

Cover photograph by: Margaret Dyches-Viles

PREFACE

There is nothing more discouraging to collectors and dealers than finding a wonderful trunk or box filled with unidentified doll clothes. Today collecting modern dolls involves identifying and locating original clothing and accessories for a specific doll. As the years roll by, it becomes harder to find these wonderful well-designed wardrobes for the dolls made from 1957-1965.

There have always been some periods in history where fashion could be described by the word "glamourous." This was such a time. It was a time of affluence, pent-up demand for consumer goods, release from world tensions and wonderful new technology in the manufacture of both man-made and natural cloth. It was also a time of great changes in women's fashions and career opportunities. These changes were reflected in the doll industry and doll designers followed the trends carefully. This book is devoted to the glamourous and other wonderful dolls of the era and their wardrobes.

By 1957 careers began to open up for girls. While they still expected to become wives and mothers, they also dreamed of being a glamourous fashion model, airline stewardess, nurse, ballerina or television star. All of these careers offered fashion possibilities. Most of these fashionable women wore high heels which were mirrored in the dolls made with molded high-heeled feet. High-heeled shoes could easily be put on and worn by many of the new dolls.

This was also a time when the women of the United States discovered the home permanent and hair care was no longer a luxury. Even little girls were given permanents by their mothers. They, too, wanted to be glamourous. Naturally, these little girls wanted combs, curlers and even permanents for their dolls. Both mothers and children loved the more expensive new rooted hair on dolls. Hair could be washed and curled, and the little girls could practice their own hair care by styling their dolls.

Not only did the dolls follow the grown-up fashion, but so did the little girls. They wanted their own "dress-up" fashions. The Little Lady Company started to make plastic high-heeled plastic shoes for children's play and soon had sold a million pairs. Other dress-up clothes were quickly added. (See *Illustration 1, Toys and Novelties,* April 1958.)

Throughout doll history there have always been some dolls fortunate enough to have wardrobes. However, from the time of *Ginny*® until the present, there has been an explosion of available wardrobes to purchase for all types of dolls.

These wonderful dolls and clothes from 1957-1965 were part of Pam's childhood. She had the plastic high heels and a mock fur stole. Today they continue to fascinate the many younger doll collectors who loved the glamourous *Revlons*®, *Barbies*®, and all the other wonderful dolls with their fashionable wardrobes.

Ginny® is a registered trademark of Vogue Dolls, Inc.
Revlon® is a registered trademark of Revlon, Inc.
Barbie® is a registered trademark of Mattel, Inc.

Illustration 1. Toys and Novelties, April 1958.

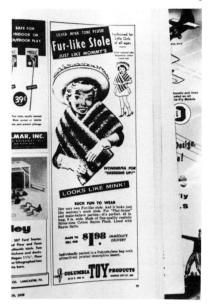

Illustration 2. Toys and Novelties, June 1958.

DOLLS FOUND IN THIS BOOK

This book concentrates on the dolls listed below. Many came with wardrobes which could be purchased separately.

1. Teenage dolls
2. Adult dolls
3. Little girl and boy dolls
4. Large dolls 30in (76cm) and over

Babies and toddlers were eliminated for the purpose of space. However, the reader should be aware that babies were popular and their clothing was lovely.

Also included in this book are individual dolls which followed the fashion trends from New York, Paris and California or were featured on television. The children who played with these dolls were the first TV generation.

Personality dolls such as *Jacqueline*® (Kennedy) are included as well as one-of-a-kind dolls dressed to reflect the clothes of the period.

While this book has a few hard plastic dolls, the focus is on rigid vinyl, vinyl and plastic dolls. Hard plastic dolls of this era such as *Ginny*®, *Betsy McCall*®, *Ginger*®, *Jill*®, *Cissy*®, *Cissette*® and others can be found in our first book, *Hard Plastic Dolls*.

Jacqueline®, *Cissy*® and *Cissette*® are registered trademarks of the Alexander Doll Co., Inc.

Ginny® and *Jill*® are registered trademarks of Vogue Dolls, Inc.

Ginger® is a registered trademark of Cosmopolitan Toy and Doll Corporation.

Betsy McCall® is a registered trademark of McCall Corp.

HOW TO USE THIS BOOK

This book is set up in several ways, depending upon your knowledge of a doll. If the doll is marked and you know the company name, turn immediately to the doll company section and look up the company name which is in alphabetical order. You will find a list of dolls and their characteristics, dates of production if possible, and a current price range.

If the doll is marked, but you do not know the company name (Example "U"), turn to the Doll Marks Section on page 233, and you will find that these marks usually indicate the Uneeda Company. Then turn to the Uneeda section for more references.

If the doll is unmarked, or if the mark is not listed, turn to the Table of Contents where you will find the page number of many doll characteristics which are listed in the Identification Guide at the end of the book.

To the amazement of the authors, research indicated to us that the height of the dolls shown in this book was often a key to the identity. For this reason the height chart is first in the Identification Guide.

Along with these physical characteristics, there are lists of ways to identify dolls by the fashions and trends during 1957 to 1965. These pages also will help you know and understand your dolls better.

The authors realize all the dolls of the period are not listed in this book. Even as we write this, much to our excitement, we have discovered new facts to help your identification. We hope you have as much pleasure searching through this book as we have had writing it. We also hope you contact us through Hobby House Press, Inc., with new information that will help in our constant search.

SYSTEM USED FOR PRICING DOLLS AND CLOTHES FOR DOLLS

The prices given include the doll and an original outfit with its accessories. A range of prices is given because some outfits make the doll more valuable than others.

In any period rare dolls or costumes are more expensive than those which can be found readily. It must also be remembered that a doll may be scarce in one section of the country and not in another.

Dolls that were presumed to be rare have a way of appearing after a book is published showing their pictures and prices. When this happens, collectors and dealers will have to adjust the prices on a downward scale.

Most of the dolls shown in this book are only valuable today because of their original mint clothing. Undressed dolls and dolls without original clothes are worth less than half the prices listed in this book.

Since 1988 when this book was first published there has been an amazing change in the desirability of these dolls. *Barbie*® has led the way with a dramatic price rise. The other fashion dolls have followed the trend and become much more valuable. They are still "good buys." *Tressy*™, for example, had as many or more accessories with her excellent clothes as *Barbie*®. Other companies competing with Mattel made unusual clothes to be used on quality dolls. These remain to be discovered as the prices of *Barbie*® and her clothes soar.

This is the first revision of the prices in this *Glamour Dolls of the 1950s & 1960s* book. These prices are listed in the back of this book. It is interesting to compare the first price with the new ones.

PRICES OF CLOTHING AND ACCESSORIES

During the 1950s and 1960s, stores that sold dolls also sold clothing for most of the dolls. Some *Barbie* outfits mint-in-box command up to $300-$1000. Madame Alexander clothes are also expensive. *Shirley Temple* mint clothes can cost hundreds of dollars.

However, readers have been sending letters telling us about the mint-in-box clothing they have been finding for dolls made in the Orient that are very nice and much less costly.

Other readers have been telling us of the joys of collecting the clothing piece-by-piece through the piles of clothes at doll shows, garage sales, etcetera, and finding the missing parts they need of these glamorous costumes. That way collectors can not only "save" money, but they can also piece together very expensive doll outfits.

At this period of doll history, these are the "fun" dolls of collectors. The authors' mail asking about these dolls has been rapidly increasing. However, like the hard plastic dolls, it is becoming more and more difficult to find both the dolls and clothes because they were made for such a short time.

Arranbee *Coty Girl.* (See page 72.)

Vogue *Jeff.* (See page 222.)

American Character *Toni.*
(See page 53.)

Virga *Schiaparelli Go Go.* (See page 220.)

Walt Disney's Horsman *Cinderella.* (See page 121.)

Mattel *Barbie* "Ski Queen." Mattel *Ken* "Ski Champion." (See page 160.)

Two Effanbee *Honey Walkers.* (See page 98.)

Cosmopolitan *Little Miss Ginger*. (See page 84.)

Ideal *Tammy*. (See page 132.)

Alexander *Caroline*. (See page 42.)

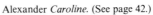

Effanbee *Mickey.* (See page 97.)

Sayco *Miss America Pageant Doll.* (See page 204.)

American Character *Toni.* (See page 55.)

Vogue *Angel* Dolls. (See pager 227.)

Alexander *Cissette.* (See page 37.)

Alexander *Elise.* (See page 35.)

Eegee *Luv-able Skin* Doll.
(See page 92.)

Alexander *Kelly* and *Edith, the
Lonely Doll.* (See page 38.)

American Character *Tressy* in her Fashion Shop. (See page 64.)

Brevete *GeGe.* (See page 78.)

Horsman *Couturier's Lady*.
(See page 117.)

Ideal *Glamour Misty*. (See page 133.)

Uneeda Girl in Red Dress.
(See page 210.)

Ideal *Pepper*. (See page 134.)

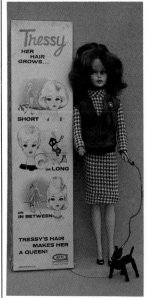

American Character *Tressy* dressed in "Blue Ribbon Winner" outfit. (See page 61.)

Ideal *Revlon Doll.* (See page 125.)

1957-1965 FASHION OVERVIEW

The authors enjoyed researching the fashions of 1957 to 1965. Perhaps, most of all, they enjoyed reminiscing about each doll as it was added to this book. Each of us had our own vision of these clothes. Pam viewed them as a child. Polly viewed them as a mother. It was a unique experience!

This section is a trip down memory lane pointing out the clothes that were widely worn, and now are kept alive through dolls. For each fashion or accessory remembered, the illustration number of one or two dolls will be given. Hopefully, the readers will discover many more illustrations of each style in their own dolls as well as those shown in this book.

High-heeled doll shoes were very important in this period. It started modestly enough in the doll world with the high-heeled Alexander *Cissy*. (See *Illustration 10.*) In 1957 Madame Alexander introduced *Elise* who had both moderate and high-heeled shoes. (See *Illustrations 11-14.*) In 1957 Cosmopolitan made a *Ginger* with a "ChaCha" heel and a *Little Miss Ginger* with a very high heel. (See *Illustration 115.*) Mothers could decide which was appropriate for their own child.

There was an infinite variety of the high-heeled shoes during the period as the advertisements of the Mary Hoyer Doll Mfg. Co. show. In 1957 *Vicky* was poised high on the "spike" heel to go with her very full skirt, and in 1965 *Vicky* was solidly posed on low heels with her Jacqueline Kennedy inspired knitted sheath. (See *Illustrations 196* and *197.*)

During much of the 1950s decade, skirts were full, being made from four to five yards of material, and were held in a whirl position by one or more crinoline petticoats. Hoops were often used, as long as the tubing line did not show. It is difficult to imagine a nurse with this type of skirt, but Cosmopolitan succeeded with their uniform for *Miss Ginger*. (See *Illustration 110.*) The Arranbee Coty Brochure showed several examples of the wonderful full skirts. (*Miss Coty* — see *Illustration 84.*) Black and white were the "safe" colors and black was the ultimate in elegance as *Miss Coty* demonstrates.

Along with the full skirt, the second silhouette was a long, straight skirt. (American Character *Toni* — see *Illustration 41, Charleston.*) Both could be seen on "Bandstand," the popular television show which featured Dick Clark.

In the summer there was very little air conditioning and the checked sundress was popular for adults and children alike. (Alexander *Carolyn* — see *Illustration 24.*) Of course, the teenagers added the high heels to attend the Fourth of July picnic.

Cissy® and *Elise*® are registered trademarks of the Alexander Doll Co., Inc.

Ginger® and *Little Miss Ginger*® are registered trademarks of the Cosmopolitan Toy and Doll Corporation.

Vicky® is a registered trademark of the Mary Hoyer Doll Mfg. Co.

Toni® is a registered trademark of The Gillette Co.

Carolyn® and *Brenda Starr*® are registered trademarks of the Alexander Doll Co., Inc.

Coty® is a registered trademark of Coty Div., Pfizer.

By the winter of 1959, fake furs were popular and many of the dolls included them in their wardrobes. Many of the stylish lady dolls marked "14R" wore fur coats or stoles. (See *Illustration 155*.) The luxurious Bambury wool coats were worn by at least two dolls. (Ideal's *Shirley Temple®* — see *Illustration 217* and Horsman's *Tweedie®* — see *Illustration 187*.)

Women wore brassieres and a girdle or garter belt. Many of the dolls in this book wear these under their clothes. (Horsman's *Cindy®* — see *Illustration 182*.) and the 1964 basic Alexander *Brenda Starr®* wore the latest in undergarments called a chemise (see *Illustration 27*). The women who struggled with seams in their stockings love the high-heeled dolls of this period.

During this period the women and girls became more active in sports and many types of sportswear developed. The early 1957 fashion dolls had only a few sports clothes, but by 1965 such a well known designer as Oleg Cassini was designing wonderful sportswear for dolls as well as fashionable women around the world. (*Tina Cassini®* — see *Illustration 352*). The sportswear for dolls during the late 1950s included pedal pusher pants pictured in several doll brochures (Ideal's *Miss Revlon®*, see *Illustration 213*, fifth from left). Rolled up dungarees (better known as jeans) were worn by many dolls but best illustrated by the *Miss America Doll®* (Sayco — see *Illustration 374*). Many dolls wore toreador pants (Virga's *Schiaparelli®* — see *Illustration 411* and Alexander's *Elise®* — see *Illustration 12*). Other sportswear included Capri pants, abbreviated shorts, halters and stretch lastex-fitted bathing suits that never can be forgotten.

But even as *Barbie®* burst onto the scene with her first full-skirted fashion, her shorter sheath dresses foreshadowed the predominant Jacqueline-look of the early 1960s. Both styles were included in the introductory 1959 wardrobe (Mattel — see *Illustration 266*). The predominant look of the early years of the "sixties" was the uncluttered look of Jackie Kennedy. The women of the United States embraced the youthful occupants of Camelot and the "fussy fashions of the fifties" were pared down. The hats became pillboxes and the classic two-piece suit had a semi-fitted top ending just below the waist (see *Illustration 22*).

Jackie loved horses and we soon all owned jodhpurs even though we did not own a horse. Madame Alexander immortalized the pictures of Jackie and Carolyn riding together when she designed her famous riding outfits for the mother and daughter (see *Illustration 23*).

Oleg Cassini was Jackie's designer and his clothes for the doll named after his daughter, Tina, reflected his designs for Jacqueline. The brochure of doll fashions (see *Illustrations 353-364*) is a modified overview of the 1960 to 1965 period. It is all there, the young look. It included the high hemline and the lower heeled shoes. The narrow skirt gave way to the A-line skirt and the trapeze dress. The sportswear included car coats, bell-bottom pants, capes with no sleeves and crop-top blouses which did not need to be tucked in. Stretch knits allowed an easier fit and as our life-style changed, so did the dolls.

The wonderful fashions of Madame Alexander followed the trends with exquisite taste. Her 1964 *Polly*® not only was made of a unique poseable body, but she was dressed in a "pared down but still beautiful" look (see *Illustration 33*).

Through the entire period, as continues today, the classic and beautiful ball dress for both women and dolls drew the attention of the talented designers of the period. Schiaparelli, designing for Virga, made the exquisite dress for the 8in (20cm) doll. Each detail makes it a vision in pink tulle (Virga — see *Illustration 412*). The ball gowns of *Barbie*® (Mattel — see *Illustration 270*) and *Miss Seventeen*® (Marx — see *Illustration 264*) and the other fashion dolls in this book are as wonderful and as collectible as those from any other period in doll history.

Throughout the entire period, the children and their mothers loved the wonderful formal bride dresses. The Alexander *Elise*® had gorgeous bride dresses each year. The *Polly*® bride of 1964 had beautiful traditional details (Alexander — see *Illustration 32*). Both came just before the "mini" and "hippie" fashion period and remind us that dolls and brides do help us remember and understand a different and more gentle world.

There is so much more to see and know about this wonderful fashion period; we hope collectors, dealers and all doll lovers will enjoy browsing and reminiscing about the fads and fashions of another era. For the "very young" new collectors, we hope you learn that all dolls are part of living history and that the dolls you love today will be part of your very own living history tomorrow.

A & H Dolls

The registered trademarks, the trademarks and the copyrights appearing in italics within this chapter belong to A&H Dolls unless otherwise noted.

Illustration 3.

Gigi: Vinyl; 10½in (27cm); jointed at neck, shoulders, waist and hips; rooted brunette hair that could be combed and curled; sleep eyes; high-heeled feet; original costume worn by Gigi Perreau in the movie; had 12 extra costumes sold separately; 1957.

Gigi was pictured as a bride in *McCall's Needlework* Fall-Winter magazine.

MARKS: None.

SEE: *Illustration 3. Toys and Novelties,* September 1957.

PRICE: $35-40 (all original)

Illustration 4.

Marcie: Vinyl; 11½in (29cm); *Barbie®* look-alike; fully jointed; rooted hair; came with trousseau; doll dressed in striped bathing suit; 1962.

SEE: *Illustration 4. Playthings,* March 1962.

PRICE: $15 (doll alone)
$35-40 (wardrobe set)

Barbie® is a registered trademark of Mattel, Inc.

Active Doll Corp.

The registered trademarks, the trademarks and the copyrights appearing in italics within this chapter belong to Active Doll Corp.

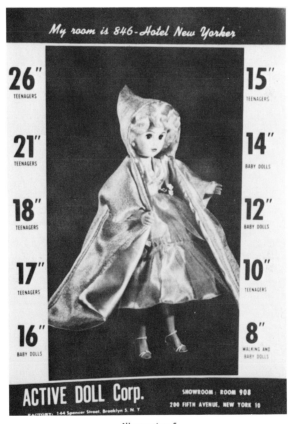

Illustration 5.

Teenage Doll: Vinyl; 10in (25cm), 15in (38cm), 17in (43cm), 18in (46cm), 21in (53cm) and 26in (66cm); rooted hair; high-heeled feet; 1958.

   SEE: *Illustration 5. Toys and Novelties,* March 1958.

   PRICE: $25-35

Admiration Toy Co., Inc.

The registered trademarks, the trademarks and the copyrights appearing in italics within this chapter belong to Admiration Toy Co., Inc.

Bride: Vinyl teenage doll; 20in (51cm); rooted hair; sleep eyes; high-heeled shoes; dressed in bridal gown with veil; available in six pastel colors; 1961.
  SEE: *Illustration 6. Toys and Novelties*, February 1961.
  PRICE: $25-40

Illustration 6.

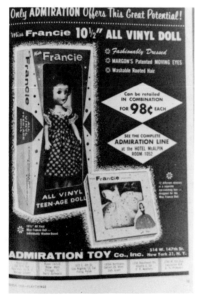

Illustration 7.

Miss Francie: All vinyl; 10½in (27cm); Margon moving eyes; washable rooted hair; circle P type; high-heeled fashion doll; wardrobe consisted of 12 dresses which could be purchased individually; 1958.
  SEE: *Illustration 7. Playthings*, March 1958.
  PRICE: $20-25

Alexander Doll Co., Inc.

Madame Alexander has always been a leader in fashion, and by 1952 was making beautiful "grown-up" dolls which were very popular. In 1955 she introduced the high-heeled mature *Cissy* with the innovative jointed arms. The Alexander catalog called *Cissy* "A Child's Dream Come True." The idea foreshadowed children's play for the next ten years.

Madame Alexander said, "Every little girl dreams of being grown up. There is no one who hasn't seen a child walking around in mother's high heels. A bra, too, and a dress or negligee can turn a hum-drum play day into a wonderful land of make-believe for a child. Now she can have all these unbelievable things in a doll to play with. *Cissy*, the doll with the figure and features of a debutante, is the newest and most exciting doll in the world. Her long slim body, her delicately molded bosom, her beautifully shaped feet that wear only high-heeled shoes made just for her and her elegant costumes designed for her alone, make *Cissy* the shining wonder of the doll world."

Cissy was an immediate success and the well-proportioned *Lissy* with a medium heel was added to the line in 1956. The tiny, slim high-heeled *Cissette*, which was made from 1957 to 1963, wore marvelous fashion clothes. Some of the outfits duplicated *Cissy's* and some of her clothes were designed for *Cissette* alone. Some clothes could be purchased separately. Although these dolls are hard plastic, one picture of each of these dolls is included in this book. Other pictures can be seen in *Hard Plastic Dolls*.

This book includes other Alexander fashion dolls from 1957 to 1965 and features the hard plastic *Elise* with vinyl arms who was introduced in 1957 and produced through 1964.

The emphasis in this book is on fashion and the wonderful clothes of these years. Included is a list of clothes for dolls that were featured in the yearly Alexander catalogs. It must be remembered that Alexander made other clothes and accessories which were not listed and could be purchased where Alexander dolls were sold. Most of them were labeled and they were as carefully designed, with attention to detail, as the clothes worn by the original dolls.

From the 1957 full-skirted dresses for *Elise* to the 1964 sheath of *Brenda Starr* and the shorter, skimpier dresses of *Polly* and *Leslie* in 1965, Madame Alexander mirrored the "grownup world of fashion design." She did, however, bring her own flair to the doll creations with the deep understanding of childhood and the play and dreams of children.

Barbara Jane: Stuffed vinyl head, arms, legs; cloth body; 29in (74cm); sleep eyes; hair can be washed, combed, curled and set; dressed in various little girl fashions in organdy or polished cotton; 1950. This mold was used for several different dolls including *Alice in Wonderland.*

Madame Alexander was usually ahead of the rest of the doll manufacturers. This is one of the first of the large stuffed vinyl dolls which became so popular in the late 1950s and early 1960s.

SEE: *Illustration 8. Playthings,* October 1950.

PRICE: $300-325 (If doll is discolored, price will be considerably lower.)

BARBARA JANE
The Life-size Playmate Doll
With the true-life realism of all Madame Alexander Creations

Illustration 8.

Illustration 9.

Penny: Stuffed vinyl head, arms, legs; cloth body; 31in (79cm); painted eyes with eyeshadow; red organdy dress with lace; blonde tight ringlets; straw hat; came with various outfits; some dolls were slightly larger and had different hair; same face as *Barbara Jane*; circa 1951-52.

Penny was inspired by Harry Haenigsen's comic strip "Penny." This was one of the first comics about bobby-soxers and their friends and families.

MARKS: "Alexander" (head)

SEE: *Illustration 9. Betty Shriver Collection.*

PRICE: $350-400 (If doll is discolored, price will be considerably lower.)

Cissy: Hard plastic head and body; vinyl arms; 20in (51cm) jointed at neck, shoulders, above elbows, hips, above knees; high heeled; sleep eyes with painted eyelashes below eyes; feathered eyebrows; pink print dress with deeper pink stripes and roses; very full skirt of period; full slip with rows of crinoline sewn on front bottom and back bottom of slip; straw hat with flowers; green sandals; 1955-1959.

Madame Alexander made many extra clothes and accessories for *Cissy* each year during the years of production. *Cissy's* clothes reflected a more mature style than most of the earlier Alexander dolls.

MARKS: "Alexander" on head; none on body; some Cissy dolls were marked "Mme Alexander" on body; " '*Cissy'*// by Madame Alexander" tag on dress.

SEE: *Illustration 10.*

PRICE: $250-300 (in street clothes)
$350-700 (in formal dresses)

Illustration 10.

Elise: Hard plastic body and head; vinyl arms; 16½in (42cm); sleep eyes; jointed at neck, shoulders, arms, hips, knees; can wear high or low shoes; introduced in 1957 to compete with other fashion dolls which featured a new "grown-up" look. *Elise* was very popular. With only minor changes in body structure, *Elise* was produced through 1964. Extra clothes and accessories could also be purchased. In 1966 there was an entirely new *Elise.*

Illustration 11.

Elise: For general characteristics, see page 33; black velvet toreador pants; white lace blouse; sash of blue starched chiffon; 1958. This was one of the extra costumes in the Alexander "separates" line.

> **MARKS:** "Elise//Madame Alexander" (clothes)
> **SEE:** *Illustration 12.*
> **PRICE:** $250-275 (doll)
> $ 60-70 (boxed clothes)
> $ 7-10 (Alexander shoes alone)

Illustration 13.

Elise Bridesmaid: For general characteristics, see page 33; long party dress or bridesmaid's dress of cotton pink nylon net; bouffant skirt over wide petticoats; pink satin sash; square neckline with white lace; hair modeled in ringlets; pearl necklace and matching bracelet; crown of flowers in hair; 1957.

> **SEE:** *Illustration 11. Nancy Roeder Collection.*
> **PRICE:** $325-350

Illustration 12.

Coco: 21in (53cm); plastic/vinyl; pink organza ball gown; 1966.

> **MARKS:** "Alexander" on head
> **SEE:** *Illustration 13. Evelyn Weibul Collection.*
> **PRICE:** $2000-2200

Illustration 14.

Elise Ballerina: Hard plastic head and body; vinyl arms; 16½in (42cm); tutu of nylon tulle; bodice of sequins to match ornate coronet; new patented wig which could be washed, combed, curled; 1962.

> **MARKS:** "MME//ALEXANDER"(back of body); "Madame Alexander" in circle (head); "3261" upside down (head)
>
> **SEE:** *Illustration 14. Marianne Gardner Collection.*
>
> **PRICE:** $200-300 (Depending on costume)

Elise: For general characteristics, see page 33; dressed in formal gown of brocade; fully-lined satin opera coat with bow; head has bandeau of white roses; jewels including ring and earrings; 1963.

This is an example of a rare mint-in-box *Elise*. Ordinary prices for *Elise* dolls do not apply and prices will vary upward as much as $1000-1100.

SEE: *Illustration 15. Christine Lorman Collection.*

PRICE: Not enough samples available.

Illustration 15.

The costumes of the first *Elise* included:

1957
1. Bride with nylon tulle gown with matching chapel length veil held by coronet of flowers.
2. Ballerina tutu of nylon tulle, attached bodice of satin; decorated with flowers; pink tights; satin ballet slippers.
3. Bridesmaid dress of dotted nylon net with a square neckline edged with lace; satin sash; carried basket of flowers.
4. Chocolate velvet coat; lined with pink taffeta; pink taffeta dress; cocoa brown hat trimmed with pale pink roses.
5. Checked taffeta street dress with puff sleeves trimmed with nylon lace; little girl collar; nylon hose; strap sandals.
6. Cocoa brown jumper dress; pink crepe shirt with bow; gold charm bracelet; cocoa brown hat.
7. Many separate clothes available for basic doll wearing lace chemise; long nylon hose; mules trimmed with lace and flowers.

1958
1. Elegant bridal gown of sheer tulle embroidered in bridal wreath design with draped bodice; tulle floor length veil attached to coronet of flowers.

2. Long dress of shadow-printed nylon with satin sash; picture hat with roses.
3. Long dance net dress trimmed with tiny rosebuds; dotted net stole; nosegay of roses at shoulder.
4. Ballerina tutu of nylon tulle; satin bodice; ruff of pleated tulle outlining decolletage; headdress of flowers with flowers on bodice also; ballet slippers.
5. Street dress of dark cotton with white pin dots; straw hat with veil.
6. Separate clothes and accessories available including velvet toreador pants with lace blouse and sash of starched chiffon.

1959
1. Pink bride dress of nylon tulle; long tulle veil with coronet of flowers; puffed sleeves; matching bridal bouquet; pearl jewels; solitaire engagement ring.
2. Bridesmaid's gown of pleated nylon with flowers on the bodice; velvet sash; pearl necklace; picture hat.
3. Nylon dress described in 1958 section with straw hat.
4. Gold ballerina tutu with layers of gold net; bodice of gold cloth with yoke of gold sequins; matching tiara; pink tights; gold ballet slippers; tiny gold and brilliant earrings.
5. Separates include nylon petticoat worn under separates; printed sateen skirt; lace-trimmed nylon blouse; crushed taffeta belt; flower-trimmed straw hat; jeweled earrings and pendant.
6. Walt Disney's *Sleeping Beauty* dressed in blue satin trimmed with gold; gold tiara trimmed with rhinestone stars; golden cape of brocaded net; rhinestone necklace and ring.

1960
Alexander advertised in their catalog that *Elise* was made of So-Lite plastic material. Her arms were still vinyl and she was jointed at the ankle, knee, hip, elbow, shoulder and neck. Her curled hair is Saran.
1. Cornflower blue ball gown of pleated nylon tulle trimmed with rosebuds and rhinestones; flowers in hair; rhinestone earrings and necklace.
2. White satin bridal gown with full skirt which is lined, giving it body; simple bodice with white lace bertha sprinkled with sequins and crystal beads; earrings; solitaire engagement ring.
3. Ballet tutu of pink nylon tulle with satin bodice trimmed with rosebuds and rhinestones stars; coronet of flowers; nylon tights; real ballet slippers.

1961
This year *Elise* changed her body structure again. She had a fully-jointed body of hard plastic, soft vinyl arms and head. She still had sleep eyes with lashes and she is jointed at the ankle, knee, hip, elbow, shoulder and neck.
1. Tulle bridal gown with floor length veil; bridal bouquet; new short wavy hairdo; engagement ring; pearl necklace; earrings.
2. Bridesmaid tulle gown with satin sash and corsage; picture hat of horsehair braid; shiny jewelry.
3. Ballerina tutu of tulle with taffeta bodice; very different classic hairdo which is upswept into a topknot of curls; coronet of flowers; long tights; ballet slippers.

1962
1. Bridal gown of nylon tulle and cobwebby lace; veil falls from coronet to floor; pearl necklace; engagement ring; bridal bouquet.
2. Ballet tutu of nylon tulle; bodice of sequins to match ornate coronet; new patented wig which could be washed, combed and curled.

1963
1. Bridal gown with layers of lace-trimmed nylon tulle; floor length veil falling from

coronet of flowers which matches bridal bouquet; engagement ring; pearl necklace and earrings; patented wig.

2. Renoir costume of mauve taffeta trimmed with lace; silk braid with reticule to match; cameo brooch; engagement ring and earrings; white straw hat trimmed with field flowers and pink veil; patented wig.

3. *Scarlett* with black hair; white skin; red cheeks; organdy gown trimmed with lace, tucks and rosebuds; large picture hat with red roses.

4. Ballet tutu of nylon tulle flaring above nylon tights; satin ballet slippers match the costume color; small roses decorate tutu; wreath of flowers in hair.

5. Riding outfit with boots and cap; checked coat with plain jodhpurs.

6. Debutante doll with checked shirt with matching shorts; wrap-around skirt of corduroy lined with taffeta; high-heeled shoes; nylon hose; unusual blonde wig style; earrings.

7. *Queen Elizabeth II of England* in brocade ball gown decorated with Order of the Bath; jewels; shining hair; tiara; long gloves.

1964

1. Bride dress with tiers of white lace in full skirt, bodice and sleeves; chapel-length veil fastened with cluster of orange blossoms; white satin bow at waist; engagement ring; pearl necklace; bridal bouquet; earrings; new wig in softly curled casual style.

2. Ballet tutu of nylon tulle and satin trimmed with flowers; ballet slippers; long tights.

Cissette: Hard plastic; 10in (25cm); high heeled; jointed at neck, shoulders, hips and knees; blue sleep eyes; eight painted eyelashes under eyes; red lips and fingernails; pearl earrings; brown bubble cut wig. *Cissette* came with many fashion ensembles of the period; original clothes styled after Jacqueline Kennedy; red sheath and jacket lined with white; white stockings; white net pillbox hat with red flower; black shoes. (See *Hard Plastic Dolls* for more information, page 27) 1962-1963.

    MARKS: "Mme Alexander" (back).

    SEE: *Illustration 16.*

    PRICE: $275-300+ (rare bubble cut *Cissette;* made for one year only).

Illustration 16.

Illustration 17.

Kelly: Rigid vinyl with soft vinyl head 15in (38cm); 16in (41cm); 22in (56cm); rooted hair; sleep eyes with real lashes; closed-mouth; individual fingers with 3rd and 4th finger curved inward; jointed at neck, shoulders, hips; contrasting dress of blue and white stripes with a plain blue cotton underdress; straw hat with ribbon bow; white socks; black slippers; *Kelly* was made only in 1958 and 1959. A different, varied wardrobe was made each year. A 12in (31cm) hard plastic doll named *Kelly* had some of the following wardrobe made for the larger dolls.

> **MARKS:** "Madame Alexander" in circle (head); "19(upside down)58" and "Madame Alexander 1958" in circle. (body)
> **SEE:** *Illustration 17.* (doll on left)
> **PRICE:** $300-325 (16in [41cm])
> $325-375 (22in [56cm])

Additional clothes included:
1958
1. Checked cotton dress with val lace and buttons; satin hair ribbon; two sizes.
2. Plain cotton coat dress with val lace and buttons; natural Milan straw roller hat with velveteen streamers; two sizes.
3. Fluffy nylon party dress trimmed with val lace; matching hat; two sizes.
4. Fine fully-lined wool coat worn over a nylon dress; fine imported Milan straw hat; larger two sizes only.
1959
1. Fine checked cotton dress with simply cut pinafore; three sizes.
2. Nylon sheer print party dress with lace; satin sash with matching hair bow; lace-edged taffeta lingerie; party slippers; socks; earrings; three sizes.
3. Puffed-sleeved organdy dress with lace; pinafore of all-over Swiss embroidery; straw hat with ribbon bow; tiny earrings; 22in (56cm) large size only.
4. Sheer nylon pleated skirt trimmed with val lace; wide satin sash; straw hat; tiny corsage of flowers; three sizes.

Edith, the Lonely Doll: From the book by Dare Wright featured in *Life Magazine*; came in two sizes, 16in (41cm) and 22in (56cm); same doll as *Kelly*; clothes came in two sizes; rigid vinyl body; soft vinyl head with rooted ponytail; sleep eyes with real lashes; dressed in pink and white checked dress; gold loop earrings; black suede shoes; 1958-1959.

> **MARKS:** "Madame Alexander" in circle (head); "19(upside down)58" and "Madame Alexander 1958" in circle (body).
> **SEE:** *Illustration 17.* (doll on right)
> **PRICE:** $275-335 (16in [41cm])
> $320-375 (22in [56cm])

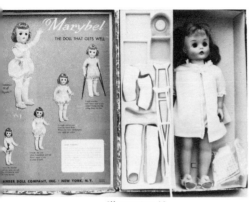

Illustration 18.

Marybel: Body, arms and legs are So-Lite plastic; vinyl head; 16in (41cm); same doll as *Kelly*; Saran wig; jointed at shoulders, arms, waist, hips; sleep eyes; came with crutches, arm casts, leg casts, bandages, band-aids, spots for measles and spots for chicken-pox; dressed in short nylon pajamas, house slippers, housecoat; 1959-1965. *Marybel* was advertised as, "The beautiful doll who gets well of her make-believe accidents and diseases."

This doll was manufactured for six years and the Alexander Company advertised it widely. The prices reflect availability to collectors today.

MARKS: "Mme Alexander" in circle with "c" in the middle// 196 (upside down) 2 (head); no marks on body.

SEE: *Illustration 18.*

PRICE: $125-150 (doll)
$175-200 (doll in case)

Pollyanna: Body, arms and legs of So-Lite plastic; head of vinyl; 16in (41cm); 22in (56cm); jointed at neck, shoulders, legs; dress of dark pink polished cotton trimmed with braid; straw hat with black ribbons and colored flowers; high-buttoned shoes; 1960.

Pollyanna also came with a polished cotton pinafore dress and high-buttoned shoes; 1960.

SEE: *Illustration 19. Childhood doll of Pat Driggs.*

PRICE: *Pollyanna* is one of the rarer dolls in this series.
$300-350+

Illustration 19.

Marybel, Pollyanna and Edith the Lonely Doll: Separate outfits which fit these dolls:

1. Piqué lined coat trimmed with brass buttons and braid; white straw hat.
2. Dolls may listen to radio in two-piece sandy striped cotton trimmed with braid; coachman's satin robe trimmed with val lace; cotton petticoat and panties trimmed with Swiss embroidery, beading and ribbon.
3. Tea dress of flowered nylon trimmed with val lace; flowers at waist.
4. Checked nylon dress trimmed with val lace.

PRICE: $60-85 (boxed outfits)

Maggie Mixup: So-Lite plastic; vinyl arms; jointed at neck, shoulders, hips, ankles; 17in (43cm); sleep eyes; red-gold hair; freckles under each eye; feathered eyebrows; eyelashes on sides of eyes; dressed in long rose pants with pockets; pink cardigan with large pink and rose flowers; flat slippers; missing is her straw hat; Saran wig; can wear low or high heels; 1961.

Maggie Mixup was made in 1960 and 1961 only.

SEE: *Illustration 20. Peggy Sue Bealford Collection.*
PRICE: $300-350

Illustration 20.

Costumes made in 1960 include:
1. Checked cotton dress with lace-trimmed white cotton blouse; lace-edged lingerie; long black tights; Capezio-type slippers; straw hat; gold necklace.
2. Party dress of cotton with organdy top and sash; golden necklace; flower-trimmed hat; long nylon hose; flat slippers with jeweled ornaments; lace-trimmed nylon lingerie.
3. Long tailored slacks; white jersey blouse; multi-striped sash; golden necklace; straw hat; flat slippers.

1961
1. Skirt and blouse worn over taffeta petticoat and leotards; flat slippers; flower-trimmed straw hat; golden heart necklace.

Elise and *Maggie Mixup:* Separate outfits in 1961 that fit both dolls.

1. Shirtwaist polished cotton dress with pockets, cuffs and yoke of Swiss embroidery; buttoned down the front.
2. Sleeveless polished cotton dress trimmed with heavy lace; very full skirt with tight-fitting bodice.
3. Suit with pleated skirt and sleeveless cardigan of piqué; blouse of checked cotton.
4. Nylon sheer nightie with lace trim; lace bed jacket.

PRICE: $70-100 (boxed outfits)

Illustration 21.

Mimi: Head and arms of soft vinyl, body and legs of hard plastic; 30in (76cm); flirty sleep eyes; jointed at head, shoulders, wrists, hips, thighs, ankles and waist; red, tan and beige shirt; blue slacks; sandals; straw hat; bracelet and earrings of bells; made in 1961 only. This was the French fisherman's outfit. Other clothes included: a party dress; Tyrolean costume; two-piece tennis outfit. F.A.O. Schwarz had a party dress and other special outfits.

MARKS: "Mimi" (dress tagged)
SEE: *Illustration 21. Esther Borgis Collection.*
PRICE: $400-475+ (The Tyrolean costume and other special costumes may command a higher price.)

Jacqueline: Hard plastic *Cissy* body; special portrait-type molded vinyl head; vinyl arms; 21in (51cm) sleep eyes with blue eye shadow; five eyelashes at side of each eye; feathered eyebrows; "pageboy-type" hairdo; pink lipstick; painted fingernails; jointed at neck, shoulders, hips, knees; high-heeled feet; blue three-piece street suit with pillbox-type hat; black around-ankle sandals; suit in 1962 Alexander catalog.

MARKS: "Alexander//19c61" (head)
SEE: *Illustration 22.* (doll on left)
PRICE: $600-700

Caroline: For general characteristics, see *Illustration 24;* dressed in three-piece playsuit of pink corduroy; long pants; lined jacket; matching hat worn over a cotton playsuit; white oxfords; socks; playsuit in 1961 Alexander catalog.

MARKS: See *Illustration 24.*
SEE: *Illustration 22.* (center doll)
PRICE: $300-350

Illustration 22.

Jacqueline: For general characteristics, see *Jacqueline* above; hair in "flip" style; dressed in leather-like beige car jacket; green corduroy slim pants; green corduroy off-the-face hat; yellow-orange jersey blouse; 1961-1962.

This suit was not in the Alexander catalog. Madame Alexander stated in her catalog in 1962 that "space does not permit us to list all the outfits available for dolls. Write for a price list of available outfits."

MARKS: "Alexander//19C61" (head); "Jacqueline//by Madame Alexander" (tag on car coat); "Jacqueline" (paper tag attached to arm of doll).
SEE: *Illustration 22.* (doll on right)
PRICE: $600-700

Jacqueline: For general characteristics, see *Illustration 22;* wearing riding outfit with cocoa brown jodhpurs and tan-lined riding coat; boots.

Caroline: For general characteristics, see *Illustration 24;* matching riding outfit; 1962.

 SEE: *Illustration 23. Christine Lorman Collection.*

 PRICE: $ 825-850 (*Jacqueline* alone)

   $ 400-450 (*Caroline* alone)

   $1500-1700 (set)

   $ 250-275 (boxed outfit for *Jacqueline*)

   $ 125-150 (boxed outfit for *Caroline*)

Illustration 23.

Jacqueline: additional clothing:
1. Three-piece brocade short coat; fully-lined skirt; jeweled tricot blouse; jewels; pillbox-type hat of tulle.
2. Brocade ball gown with flaring red satin side panels; pearl necklace; bright earrings and ring.
3. White satin brocade full-length ball gown; lined satin evening coat.
4. Strapless silver and white brocade evening gown; matching short jacket with pearl hook at waistline.

In 1962 Marshall Field & Company featured a *Jacqueline* in a trunk with the following clothes:
1. Brocade ball gown with red satin side panels; rhinestone crown earrings.
2. Blue jersey bathing suit with terry cloth robe.
3. Pink taffeta nightgown underneath flowered robe.
4. Pink afternoon dress with lace top.
5. Blue checked cotton dress with full skirt; front buttons to waist.
6. Beige sheath dress with matching fully-lined coat.

Illustration 24.

Caroline: Rigid vinyl; soft vinyl head and arms; 15in (38cm); feathered eyebrows; sleep eyes with real lashes; painted eyelashes at side and under eyes; molded tongue in mouth; individual fingers; blonde rooted hair; dotted Swiss pink dress with attached taffeta petticoat; hair tied back with pink ribbon; white suede-like slippers; extra blue, red and white sailor pants and top in original slim package; 1961.

Additional wardrobe for *Caroline* that was listed in Alexander catalogs:

1. Organdy tea party dress with tucked lace trim; satin sash; taffeta slip with matching panties, party slippers; party socks; 1961.
2. Checked cotton dress with white organdy lace-trimmed collar; 1962.
3. Riding habit made of suede-like cocoa brown and beige material; boots; 1962.
4. Lace-trimmed organdy dress with band of colored embroidery at waistline; organdy bow; pink hair ribbon; 1962.

    MARKS: "Alexander//19c61" (back of head); "Madame Alexander//New York//All Rights Reserved" (tag of sailor suit); "Caroline" (label of Alexander box)
    SEE: *Illustration 24.*
    PRICE: $300-350 (doll)
                $100-150 (rare boxed sailor outfit)
                $ 75-125 (regular boxed outfits)

Caroline outfits which could be ordered separately:
1. Flower print nylon party dress with ruffles, lace and satin ribbon; taffeta petticoat and panties.
2. Pajamas and robe of flowered tricot.
3. Pajamas and robe of flowered cotton.
4. Play dress of cotton piqué trimmed with braid and buttons; matching panties; white slippers and socks.
5. Play dress with polka dot collar; leotards of cotton jersey.

Illustration 25.

***Pamela*,** Wardrobe and Case: Hard plastic; 12in (31cm); *Pamela* is a *Lissy* doll; hard plastic head has velour strip that makes it possible to change wigs; three wigs included were blonde braids, brown curls and blonde curls; blue sleep eyes; eight painted eyelashes under eye; red lips; wardrobe includes:

1. Ballerina outfit of pink satin tulle, white slippers, flowered headpiece.
2. Pink and white negligee.
3. Blue satin ruffled long dress trimmed with white lace.
4. Ethnic costume, white bodice, red skirt with a black overskirt, headdress.
5. Accessories include curlers, shoes, underwear, socks; 1962-63.

    MARKS: None on doll; "PAMELA" (wrist tag).
    SEE: *Illustration 25.*
    PRICE: $600-650 (in case with extra clothes)
               $175-225 (boxed clothes)

Brenda Starr: Rigid vinyl; 12in (31cm); *Barbie*® look-alike; jointed at neck, shoulders and knees; high-heeled feet; sleep eyes with lashes; blonde rooted hair which could be styled; instruction book for hair care included in gift package; black sheath with multi-colored flowers; black shoes; 1964-1965. Other clothes included:

1. Beach swimsuit of printed nylon tricot, terry cape with hood lined with suit material; flower-trimmed beach case; sunglasses, beach sandals; 1964.
2. Shirtwaist dress with collar and tiny buttons; cotton cluny lace at bottom of skirt; black opera pumps; white handbag; 1964.
3. Large flower print lined sheath; bead necklace; black pumps; 1964.
4. Basic doll has a lace chemise; mules; 1964.

MARKS: "Alexander//19c64" (head).
SEE: *Illustration 26.* (doll in dress).
      Illustration 27. (basic doll). *Gigi Williams and Sherry Baloun Collection.*
PRICE: $150-175 (doll)
     $ 50-75 (outfits)

Illustration 26.   *Illustration 27.*

Illustration 28.

Illustration 29.

Kurt from "Sound of Music": Rigid vinyl body and soft vinyl head; 11in (28cm); *Janie*-face; blue sailor suit with red trim; all original; 1964.

This is a very rare doll. *Kurt* rather than *Frederick* was included in a wrist booklet used on the dolls made for a set of "Sound of Music" dolls dressed in sailor outfits. He is fully labeled. *Kurt* was in an early "Sound of Music" discontinued set with a sailor suit theme. *Frederick* became the only boy used in later sets. *Kurt* also came with a *Smarty*-face.

MARKS: "Alexander" (head); "Kurt" (tag on suit).
SEE: *Illustration 28. Marianne Gardner Collection.*
PRICE: $650-700+ (very few sample prices)

Sound of Music: Vinyl with soft vinyl head; sleep eyes with lashes; rooted hair; 1965. Left to right, upper row:
1. *Louisa:* 14in (36cm); magenta skirt, black vest with decorations at neckline, white blouse.
2. *Maria:* 17in (43cm); white, brown, yellow, orange overskirt; suede-colored dirndle; white top; straw hat with flowers; black shoes for medium heels.
3. *Liesl:* 14in (36cm) orange dress with white sleeves; green striped apron; straw hat.
Left to right, lower row:
1. *Gretl:* 11in (28cm) dark print skirt with flower print; red jumper top with gold braid, white blouse.
2. *Brigitta:* 14in (36cm); red skirt with black jumper top with gold braid ties; white blouse; red bow in hair.
3. *Fredrick:* 11in (28cm) brown lederhosen pants with straps and yellow braid around hem of pants; white checked shirt; yellow alpine hat with braid.
4. *Marta:* 11in (28cm); beige flower print skirt; blue top with dark braid trim; white sleeves.
Each doll wears authentic colorful alpine outfits from Austria.

SEE: *Illustration 29. Joyce M. Alderson Collection.*
PRICE: $1300-1500 (set)

Katie: Soft, satiny, light brown plastic; 12in (31cm); sleep eyes with lashes; softly curling wig; hands posed in charming fashion; smile on face; yellow dress and shoes made of lovely material; all original; first in Alexander catalog in 1965. Black version of *Smarty.*

MARKS: "Alexander 1964" (head); "Katie" (dress tag).

SEE: *Illustration 30. Lanell Rowland Collection.*

PRICE: $400-450

Illustration 30.

Illustration 31.

Little Orphant Annie: Vinyl; 14in (36cm); freckles; brown print dress; apron with lace; brown suede pocketbook; 1965. The advertisement says, "The doll is based on a description of the little girl in a poem by the Hoosier poet James Whitcomb Riley...Madame Alexander, in line with the company's latest creation, was an honored guest at a recent celebration in Indianapolis, Ind. honoring the 116th birthday of James Whitcomb Riley. A replica of the original Annie doll was presented by Madame Alexander."

SEE: *Illustration 31. Toys and Novelties,* November 1, 1965.

PRICE: $350-360

Little Orphant Annie extra clothes that came with decorated window box:
1. Green and white checked gingham dress with lace and braid trim.
2. White organdy lace-edged slip.
3. Pink and white dotted swiss trimmed morning robe.
4. Set of pink hair curlers and comb.
5. A whisk broom to help her with her household chores.

PRICE: $70-90 (mint-in-box outfits)

Polly: Made for one year only in 1965. She had a hard plastic body with a vinyl head, arms and legs. She had separates which could be purchased. Like so many other dolls of the period, her arms and legs were poseable by gently bending the knees and elbows. This caused a disintegration of the vinyl around the joints. Today this bending should be done with caution.

Leslie was a black *Polly* and she could wear the same clothes as *Polly*. She also had outfits of her own. Some were very similar to those of *Polly*.

Mary Ellen Playmate also had the same mold as *Polly*. She was made for Marshall Field & Company and was featured in their 1965 catalog.

Illustration 32.

Doll on right:

Polly Ballerina: Soft vinyl which can be shaped and posed in many positions; 17in (43cm); shoulder length soft curled, dark rooted hair; turquoise permanent-pleated tutu with sequin bodice; matching panties; hair piece not original; pink satin ballet slippers; 1965.

Doll on left:

Polly in Ball Gown: Permanent-pleated pink bouffant skirt; pink sequined bodice; rose at waist; pink taffeta underskirt with ruffle; stockings; beige medium-heeled slipers; beautiful red hair; ring on finger; removable twisted chignon with ropes of sequins intertwined.

MARKS: "ALEXANDER DOLL COMPANY" (back of neck); "Polly//by Madame Alexander New York U.S.A." (tag on dress).

Polly Bride: Soft vinyl head, arms, legs; hard plastic body; 17in (43cm); can be posed by gently bending knees and elbows; sleep eyes with lashes, rooted hair; blue eyes; closed-mouth; individual fingers; dressed in layered tulle net trimmed in lace; outer layer of tulle is similar to coat; matching shoes; traditional garter; ring; beautiful chapel length veil with lovely flowers at the back of head; doll made in 1965 only; all original.

MARKS: "Alexander Doll Co., Inc.//1965" (back of neck); "Polly//Madame Alexander New York U.S.A." (dress tag)

SEE: *Illustration 32. Louise Schnell Collection.*

PRICE: $325-375

Illustration 33.

SEE: *Illustration 33.*
PRICE: $300-350 (Ballerina)
$350-400 (Ball Gown)

Polly Additional Clothes:
1. Orange-striped dress with matching polka dot ruffle; slip; panties; long stockings; ring; similar to *Leslie's* green dress.
2. White cotton lace over a light blue taffeta; taffeta panties; flat slippers; tiny bow in hair.
3. White button-down dress with red trim down the dress and around the hemline; red ribbon bow in hair and neckline of dress.
4. Deep pink chiffon formal dress with deep pleated ruffle at hemline; ruffled collar; three-quarter length sleeve.
5. Two-piece red velveteen suit; white lace on white bodice which is joined to skirt; jacket sleeves trimmed in lace; nylon stockings; red shoes; red bow in hair; ring.
6. High-waisted pink linen formal trimmed in deep cotton lace at hemline; narrow maroon sash with tiny flowers at waist; matching slippers; ring.

Additional clothing for the *Polly* dolls was exclusively sold through F.A.O. Schwarz. They sold a *Polly* doll in a trunk with clothes called *Polly on Tour.*
PRICE: $100-150 (mint-in-box outfits)

Illustration 34.

Leslie: Soft vinyl which can be shaped in various poses; 17in (43cm); sleep eyes with lashes; soft satiny brown coloring; shoulder length curly rooted hair; wearing green and white striped cotton dress with two ruffles of polka dot; small white bow at neck; slip trimmed with lace; matching shoes and stockings; ring; 1965.

SEE: *Illustration 34. Toys and Novelties,* November 15, 1965.
PRICE: $350-375 (street clothes)
$400-450 (formals)

Leslie can wear *Polly's* clothes. Her special wardrobe includes:
1. White cotton lace short evening dress with pink lining and pink taffeta slip and panties; pink satin sash and flower at waist; slippers; ring.
2. Pink formal with satin softly draped skirt; pink velvet top trimmed with pink sequins at neck; three-quarter sleeves; tiny roses at waist; glitter in hair; matching slippers; ring.
3. Yellow permanent-pleated tulle gown; yellow sequin sleeveless bodice; matching slippers; sequins in hair; ring.

PRICE: Mint in box outfits
$100-150

Joanie: So-Lite plastic body with soft vinyl head; 36in (91cm); jointed at neck, shoulders, hips; walks if you take her left hand and move her forward by pressing first one leg and then the other, heel-and-toe fashion; flirty eyes; long curly eyelashes; 1960.

Clothes:
1. Cotton dress with pearl buttons; white braid; sash tied in bow in back; nylon lingerie trimmed with ruffles of nylon tulle; black slippers; 1960.
2. Organdy dress with lace trim; pinafore tied with satin ribbon; matching hair ribbon; black patent slippers; 1960.
3. Pinafore of red polished cotton over white organdy dress; nylon lingerie; black patent slippers; 1960.
4. Nurse's uniform; white cap and apron; nylon lingerie; white oxfords; 1960-1961.
   PRICE: $375-425

Betty: So-Lite body with soft vinyl head; 30in (76cm); jointed at neck, shoulders, hips; walks when you take her by the left hand and move her forward by pressing first one leg and then the other; flirty eyes with long curly lashes; 1960-1961.

Clothes:
1. Swiss organdy trimmed with val lace; nylon lingerie; black patent slippers; 1960.
2. Classic cotton dress; lace-edged organdy collar; nylon lingerie; black slippers; 1960.
3. Cotton dress with white blouse front with buttons and folds of blue; braid-trimmed skirt; nylon lingerie; black patent slippers; 1960.
4. Dress with lined jacket to match; nylon lingerie; black patent slippers; white straw hat with flowers; 1961.
   PRICE: $375-425

Little Lady: So-Lite plastic; 8in (20cm); jointed at neck, shoulders, hips; walks; wears quaint cotton dress with pinafore; pantalets; buttoned shoes; doll is packaged in a shadow box frame for wall hanging; Little Lady Toiletries include two packs of bubble bath and one bottle of perfume; 1960.
   PRICE: $700 and up

Sweetie Walker: Very light plastic; 23in (58cm); short, straight, shining hair; walker if you lead her gently by the hand; sleep eyes; 1962.

Clothes:
1. Rose printed dress with ruffles; organdy puffed sleeves; tie shoes.
2. Dotted swiss dress; polished piqué coat; tie shoes.
   PRICE: $125-150

Melinda: Rigid vinyl; 16in (41cm) and 22in (56cm); jointed at neck, shoulders, waist, hips; long whitish hair with bangs; 1962. In 1963 a 14in (36cm) size was added.

Clothes:
1. Ruffled dress of dotted cotton trimmed with lace; white straw hat; 1962.
2. Dress with red velveteen top; skirt of lace-trimmed organdy; hat; 1962.
3. Organdy party dress trimmed with satin ribbon, rosebuds and rows of lace on skirt; satin slippers; satin hair ribbon tied with flowers; 1963.

4. Ballet tutu with satin top and tulle skirt trimmed with flowers and rhinestones; satin ballet slippers; hair arranged in classic ballet style; 1963.
5. Checked gingham dress; tucked skirt; big sash; can-can type petticoat; black shoes and white socks; 1963.
6. Organdy dress with red velvet top; puffed sleeves with three rows of lace; can-can petticoat; straw hat trimmed with flowers and lace; black shoes; 1963.
   PRICE: $350-370 (14in [36cm] and 16in [41cm])
   $375-395 (22in [56cm])

Mary Ellen Playmate: Same doll as *Polly* (see *Illustration 32*); made exclusively for Marshall Field & Company; 1965.
   PRICE: $375-425+

Patti: Plastic with vinyl head; 18in (46cm); smiling face; sleep eyes and lashes; 1965.

Clothes:
1. ™Party dress of turquoise blue; lace-ruffled trim with matching taffeta lace-trimmed slip and panties; flower spray on hair; black shoes.
2. Pink fully-lined linen dress; blue applique tulip flower trim; white shoes.
   PRICE: $350-375

Mary Ann: Plastic with soft vinyl head; 14in (36cm); called sub-teen in catalog; sleep eyes; rooted curling hair; 1965.

Clothes:
1. White piqué jumper attached to red cotton permanent-pleated skirt; white piqué panties.
2. Scotch plaid pleated skirt; white sweater and hat; red mittens; red scarf; red boots; white tights.
3. Ballerina with pleated tulle ballet dress; sequined bodice; satin ballet slippers; white tights.
   PRICE: $285-315

Yolanda: Plastic; soft vinyl head; 12in (30cm); *Barbie*®-type; jointed at neck, shoulders, hips and knees; sleep eyes; rooted silky hair arranged in a twisted chignon; 1965. (See *Brenda Starr,* page 44.)

Clothes:
1. Turquoise satin formal with sequin trim on dress and in hair.
2. Bride dress with tiers of ruffled lace; tulle veil with floral crown; pearl earrings and necklace; blue garter; bridal bouquet.
3. Permanent-pleated pink tulle formal; satin jeweled bodice.
   PRICE: $175-200 (doll)

Barbie®is a registered trademark of Mattel, Inc.

Allied-Grand Doll Mfg., Inc.

The registered trademarks, the trademarks and the copyrights appearing in italics within this chapter belong to Allied-Grand Doll Mfg. Inc., unless otherwise noted.

Toddler: 16in (41cm); vinyl; stylishly coiffured rooted ponytail; sleep eyes; leotard under skirt with straps; 1961.

SEE: *Illustration 31. Toys and Novelties, March 1961.*

PRICE: $45-50 (in this condition)

Bonnie Bride: All vinyl; 24in (61cm) fully-jointed; high heels; white satin dress trimmed with lace; net veil; clothes all original; circa 1961-1962. This doll was advertised in *Toys and Novelties,* May, 1961.

> **MARKS:** Box marked: "A Bonnie Doll" (top); "A Bonnie Doll//Honey #2955// An Allied Quality doll//Mfg. by Allied Grand Doll Mfg. Co. Inc. Brooklyn 32, N.Y." (side).
> **MARKS:** None on doll; "An Allied Quality Doll//Bonnie doll//highest quality" (wrist tag).

PRICE: $35-50

Illustration 35.

Allied made other dolls including *Barbie*® look-alikes. They were plastic and vinyl with dark arched eyebrows. One was 11½in (29cm). There were no marks. An 11in (28cm) all vinyl doll was marked "Allied Grand Doll//Mfg. Inc." There was an "A" on the lower back. They were also famous for large bride and beautiful lady dolls.

Barbie® is a registered trademark of Mattel, Inc.

American Character Doll Corporation-American Doll and Toy Corporation

The registered trademarks, the trademarks and the copyrights appearing in italics within this chapter belong to American Character Doll Corporation or American Doll and Toy Corporation, unless otherwise noted.

Illustration 36.

American Character made many, many lovely dolls during the first part of the 20th century. When high-heeled dolls became popular, they were among the leaders in the field. Their *Toni, Sweet Sue Sophisticate* and *Tressy* dolls followed the latest changes in fashion, and their large dolls such as *Little Miss Echo* were among the loveliest of the large "Playpal-type" dolls.

They advertised widely on television and published comic books that used the dolls as main characters. In May 1960 they advertised that they had changed their name to American Doll and Toy Corporation.

SEE: *Illustration 36. Playthings,* May 1960.

The Toni® Family: The *Toni* line of dolls was made by American Character to advertise and promote the Toni line of hair care products. A special characteristic of the *Toni* dolls was their beautiful rooted hair which could be washed and styled by using the special *Toni* Doll Play Wave Kit. By following the directions on the box, a child could create six different styles with the wave solution applicator, curlers, comb, brush and make-up cape that were included in the kit. Also advertised in the *Toni* brochures was the Tonette home permanent for carefree curls for little girls. The *Toni* dolls came in four sizes: 10½in (27cm), 14in (36cm), 20in (51cm) and 25in (64cm). The three larger dolls were tagged *Toni* or *Sweet Sue Sophisticate.*

Toni®: See *Illustration 38;* 10½in (27cm); "Display consists of wrought iron stand, plastic bubbles, seventeen dressed *Toni* dolls and *Toni* Doll Playwave Kit;" 1958.

SEE: *Illustration 37. Toys and Novelties,* May 1958.

PRICE: $55-70 (doll)
$25-35 boxed (outfit)

Toni® is a registered trademark of the Gillette Co.

Illustration 37.

Toni®: Rigid vinyl body, soft vinyl head; 10½in (27cm); rooted light brown hair; blue sleep eyes; two painted eyelashes at side of eyes; feathered eyebrows; red lips; jointed at shoulders, neck, hips; original boxed outfits but clothes are not tagged; Right: blue satin "balloon" dress with full gathered skirt, blue velvet bow, fur muff and hat, black sandals, Left: blue felt coat trimmed with black velvet, black velvet hat with blue ribbon, black satin skirt with white bodice trimmed in silver glitter, nylons, black sandals; circa 1958.

> **MARKS:** "AMER. CHAR DOLL CORP. 1958" in circle (back of head); "AMERICAN © CHARACTER 1958" (lower back).
> **SEE:** *Illustration 38.*
> **PRICE:** $55-70

Illustration 38.

Toni®: Hard plastic body, soft vinyl head; 10½in (27cm); high heeled; red lips; blue sleep eyes with molded lashes; two painted eyelashes at side of eyes; feathered eyebrows; jointed at neck, shoulders, hips; fingers molded separately with 3rd and 4th fingers curled; original clothes but no tag; cocktail dress with pink satin skirt with black lace overskirt, black velvet bodice, pink net cape, nylons, black sandals; dark brown rooted hair in flip style; circa 1958.

> **MARKS:** "AMER. CHAR DOLL CORP. 1958" in circle (back of head); "AMERICAN © CHARACTER" in circle (lower back).
> **SEE:** *Illustration 39.*
> **PRICE:** $55-70

Illustration 39.

Toni®: Boxed fashions for the 10½in (27cm) *Toni* doll; beige felt coat, red straw hat; red shoes and nylons in their own package; 1958.

> **SEE:** *Illustration 40.*
> **PRICE:** $25-35

Toni® is a registered trademark of The Gillette Co.

Illustration 40.

Toni® Doll Brochure: The title page reads, "The story of the new *Toni* Doll//her play wave kit//and her wonderful Fashion Wardrobe." Cartoon pictures of *Toni* clothes accompanied a cartoon story about girls and their *Toni* dolls.

Top: Description of the *Toni* Play Wave Kit and drawings of possible *Toni* hair styles.

Middle:
  1. *Toni*
  2. *Cheer Leader*
  3. *Charleston*

Bottom:
  1. *Collegiate*
  2. *Stewardess*
  3. *Tea Time*

Fashions in this illustration are for the 10½in (27cm) *Toni* doll; circa 1958.

SEE: *Illustration 41. Marybeth Manchook Collection.*

Toni® Doll Brochure: All fashions in this illustration are for the 10½in (27cm) *Toni®* doll.

Top:
  1. *Coat and Hat*
  2. *TV Time*
  3. *High Society*

Bottom:
  1. *Suburbanite*
  2. *Bon Soir*
  3. *Cha-Cha*; circa 1958

SEE: *Illustration 42. Marybeth Manchook Collection.*

Toni® Doll Brochure: Top and middle rows in this illustration are for the 10½in (27cm) doll.

Top:
  1. *Romance with Mink Stole*
  2. *Dinner Date*
  3. *Toni®* Doll with Playwave Kit

Middle:
  1. *Bride*
  2. *Cocktails*
  3. *Sunday Stroll*

Each fashion in the bottom row could be bought for either the 14in (36cm) or 20in (51cm) *Toni®*

Bottom:
  1. *Romance with Mink Stole*
  2. *Town and Country*
  3. *Ballerina*; circa 1958

SEE: *Illustration 43. Marybeth Manchook Collection.*

Toni® is a registered trademark of the Gillette Co.

Illustration 41.   *Illustration 42.*   *Illustration 43.*

Toni® Doll Brochure: All fashions in this illustration could be worn by the 14in (36cm), 20in (51cm) and 25in (64cm) *Toni* doll.

Top:
1. *Love in Bloom*
2. *Country Club*
3. *Dinner Date*

Bottom:
1. *Bride*
2. *American Beauty*; circa 1958

SEE: *Illustration 44. Marybeth Manchook Collection.*

Illustration 44.

Illustration 45.

Toni®: Rigid vinyl body, soft vinyl head; 14in (36cm); blonde rooted hair in tight flip curls; jointed at neck, shoulders, waist, hips; large blue sleep eyes with molded eyelashes; nine painted eyelashes under eyes; red lips and fingernails; high heeled; bride doll; white lace over satin dress with crinoline skirt; white satin flowers on dress; white flower bouquet tied with white ribbon; white heels; white satin cap trimmed with pearls; white net veil; circa 1958.

MARKS: None on doll.
SEE: *Illustration 45.*
PRICE: $120-140

Toni®: Rigid vinyl body and soft vinyl head; 14in (36cm); jointed at neck, shoulders, waist, hips; eye shadow above sleep eyes; eyelashes below eyes; high forehead; one line on seat (see *Hard Plastic Dolls,* page 282C); blue satin top with low wide belt, two-tiered pleated skirt; high-heeled feet; rooted hair; circa 1957.

MARKS: None on doll.
SEE: *Illustration 46. Marybeth Manchook Collection.*
PRICE: $100-130

Toni® is a registered trademark of The Gillette Co.

Illustration 46.

Illustration 47.

Toni®: Rigid vinyl body, soft vinyl head; 20in (51cm); auburn rooted hair pulled back in ponytail; high heeled; jointed at neck, shoulders, hips, waist; large blue sleep eyes; 10 painted eyelashes under right eye; 11 painted eyelashes under left eye; feathered eyebrows; red lips, finger and toenails; original clothes; midnight blue satin cocktail dress with "balloon" skirt which is gathered at the bottom; black velvet purse, white fox stole with two fox heads by the clasp; nylons, black sandals; doll came with a "*Toni®*" wrist tag; circa 1958.

MARKS: None on head; "AMERICAN © CHARACTER" in circle (lower back).
SEE: *Illustration 47.*
PRICE: $125-150

Sweet Sue Sophisticate Bride (*Toni®*): Rigid vinyl body with soft vinyl head; 20in (51cm); jointed at neck, shoulders, waist, hips; sleep eyes; rooted hair; single line on seat (see *Hard Plastic Dolls,* page 282C); fingertip veil with small satin cap on head; high-heeled feet; circa 1957.

MARKS: "American Character" in circle (head); "Sweet Sue Sophisticate//Your Grown up Doll" (tag).
SEE: *Illustration 48.* (doll) *Marybeth Manchook Collection.*
Illustration 49. (tag) *Marybeth Manchook Collection.*
PRICE: $125-150

Toni® is a registered trademark of The Gillette Co.

Illustration 48.

Illustration 49.

***Toni*®:** Rigid vinyl head and soft vinyl body; 25in (64cm); jointed at neck, shoulders, waist, hips, ankles; white nylon dress over a blue underdress; three rows or ruffles trimmed with white embroidery; blue straw hat with blue flower; high-heeled feet; circa 1957.

SEE: *Illustration 50. Pat Freeman Collection.*

PRICE: $135-165

Toni® is a registered trademark of The Gillette Co.

***Betsy McCall*®:** Rigid vinyl with soft vinyl head; 14in (36cm); rooted blonde hair; feathered eyebrows; sleep eyes with lashes and two painted lashes on corners of eyes; individual fingers with first finger slightly pointing; unusually long slender legs; jointed at neck, shoulders, waist, hips; 1958.

In the 1950s the *Betsy McCall*® dolls traditionally had brunette hair. This *Betsy McCall*® had rooted hair in several shades and the blonde was often used in the advertising. In 1959 a 20in (51cm) *Betsy McCall*® was made.

MARKS: In circle "McCall//19c5?//Corp." (head). This mark wears off easily. The last number on this doll is difficult to read.

SEE: *Illustration 51.*

PRICE: $150-175 (hard to find).

Betsy McCall® is a registered trademark of the McCall Corp.

Illustration 50.   *Illustration 51.*

Advertising Comic Books with American Dolls and Toys: In 1961 American Doll and Toy Company published a comic book entitled "How to Have Fun and Play." The children could read about the new dolls each year. The format was interesting and fun.

SEE: *Illustration 52. (Betsy McCall®, Toodles, Chuckles).*
Illustration 53. (Betsy McCall®).

Illustration 52.

Illustration 53.

Betsy McCall®: Plastic body and legs; vinyl head and arms; 22in (56cm); jointed at neck, shoulders, wrists, waist, ankles; brown eyes with three painted eyelashes at corner of eyes; pink ballerina costume; circa early 1960s.

MARKS: None on doll.

SEE: *Illustration 54. Pat Parton Collection.*

PRICE: $165-180

Betsy McCall® is a registered trademark of the McCall Corp.

Illustration 54.

Tressy, Her Hair Grows: When American Character Company presented their *Tressy* doll, there was a great demand for fashion dolls. There was also a demand for home hair products; beautiful hairdos for both women and children had become the vogue. The beautiful *Tressy* was a wonderful way to teach children about both fashionable clothes and hair styling and care.

Children watched television and dreamed about fashion careers, and *Tressy* seemed to be the "real" adult doll, not just a teenager.

The brochure which came with *Tressy* said, "From a tiny town to the huge city came *TRESSY* carrying just a suitcase full of dreams that all came true with her glamorous debut as, MISS AMERICAN CHARACTER, the most beautiful girl in the land. The magical world of hi-fashion modeling, television, the stage and gala social events welcomed her with open arms."

"*Tressy* needs high style hair-dos, stunning fashions and beautiful accessories for all her glamorous activities...from sailing and sunning to dancing and parties. Shopping and sports to modeling and traveling. Wherever *Tressy* goes, whatever she is doing, you can always be sure she will look her lovliest. Just think of the hours of fun you'll have with her exquisite hi-fashion wardrobe. Best of all, — *TRESSY'S* hair — THE HAIR THAT GROWS — can be styled in dozens of wonderful ways to match her fabulous fashion collection."

The "Secret Strand" of hair grows from the top of the head. A button on her tummy and a separate key operates the mechanism for making it short or long.

There were two different *Tressy* dolls. The first one came with heavy makeup painted on her face. The second *Tressy* was sometimes called *Mary Make-up* and came with a pale face. A cosmetic kit could be purchased and children could practice a skill that they were expected to need when they grew up. Both could be dressed in the same wardrobe.

Today, collectors are discovering the wonderful world of *Tressy*. Her clothes and accessories are elegant and well-designed. Because *Barbie®* became so popular, there are fewer *Tressy* dolls and costumes. Mint-in-box outfits are rare.

Barbie® is a registered trademark of Mattel, Inc.

Illustration 55.

Tressy dolls (close-up): *Barbie*® look-alike; left: original doll with darker high-color face and heavy eye makeup; right: "Magic Make-up" doll with pale color and no black heavy makeup or eyelashes.

For general characteristics, see *Illustrations 56* and *65*.
The doll on the left is wearing the shift which came on most boxed *Tressy* dolls.
The doll on the right is wearing the *World's Fair* outfit.
SEE: *Illustration 55.*
PRICE: $30-45 (doll on left)
            $25-30 (doll on right)

Tressy (first): Rigid plastic body and legs; rigid poseable vinyl arms; soft vinyl head; 12in (31cm); *Barbie*® look-alike; rooted hair with grow mechanism in stomach operable by a separate key which came with the doll; blue side-glancing eyes; heavy painted upper lids with four eyelashes at corners of eyes; black eyebrows; eye shadow above eyes; mold marks under wrists; jointed at neck, shoulders, hips; high-heeled feet; *Barbie*® competitor; blonde, brunette, red hair; 1963.

Tressy is dressed in *Evening Jewel*. *Bowling Beauty* outfit is shown in the picture on the right in the brochure.
MARKS: "American Doll & Toy Corp.//19c63" in circle (head).
SEE: *Illustration 56.*
PRICE: $40-45

Barbie® is a registered trademark of Mattel, Inc.

Illustration 56.

Illustration 57.

Tressy: See general characteristics for first *Tressy; Barbie*® look-alike; dressed in #30901 *Blue Ribbon Winner;* brown and white checked dress with brown cotton suede jacket; black poodle; 1963.

>   **MARKS:** "American Doll and Toy Corp.//1963" in circle (head).
>   **SEE:** *Illustration 57.*
>   **PRICE:** $50 (mint-in-box)

Barbie® is a registered trademark of Mattel, Inc.

Tressy Hair Brochure: *Tressy* tells about how her hair grows.

"My beautiful hair really grows and with a little practice you'll be able to style it dozens of ways. Now you will know the secret way to make my hair grow shorter or longer to match the hi-fashion outfits I love to wear. Just think...no matter where I go or what I wear my hair style will always be beautiful and correct.

"The part of my hair that grows is called the Secret Strand. It grows from the top of my head and is separate from my regular hair."

>   **SEE:** *Illustration 58.* (*Tressy* hair brochure).
>   *Illustration 59.* (*Tressy* hair brochure).

Illustration 58.

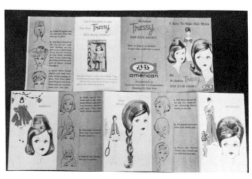

Illustration 59.

Tressy Fashions: Each of the outfits came in a "see-through" box; lovely accessories added to the basic fashion just as they did in the adult fashion world.

    MARKS: "Tressy Fashions" (packaged outfit).

    SEE: *Illustration 60. (In the Swim).*

             Illustration 61. (Surprise Party).

    PRICE: $20-30 (box)

Illustration 60.   *Illustration 61.*

Tressy Fashions: The following outfits listed in the *New Tressy* Fashion Catalog are not shown in any of the *Tressy* photographs in this book.

1. *Sleepytime Gal*   4. *Neat Knit*
2. *Chic Shift*   5. *Car Coat*
3. *Sophisticated Lady*

Tressy Hair Glamour Paks and Brochure: Left to right: Hair Glamour Pak contains pink rollers, spin curlers, rubber bands, two extra keys (Pak 1262); center: *Tressy's* own magazine of hair care; right: pak contains hair spray and two refill packages, beauty cape, extra key (1263).

    SEE: *Illustration 62.*

    PRICE: $15 (hair care kits)

Illustration 62.

Tressy, Mary Make-up, Cricket Brochure:

1. "Here's Mary Make-up...special gift and a special girl...Tressy's best friend. She is wearing her own shift. But, oh, what she can borrow from her best friend."

2. "It's Tressy...her hair grows, her legs pose! Isn't it lucky that Tressy and Mary are exactly the same size! Tressy has such lovely hi-fashion clothes and accessories to lend to her best friend."

3. "Cricket, Tressy's little sister, her hair grows too! She likes nothing better than to tag along with Tressy and Mary and act grownup. Cricket is still too small to borrow, so she has her own wardrobe and accessories. And Cricket has posing legs just like her big sister Tressy."

The brochure shows the "shift" that was on the boxed dolls. *Tressy's* wardrobe includes *Sugar 'n Spice; Pink Champagne; Blue Ribbon Winner; Hootennany; Good News; Campus Casual; Window Shopping; Executive Sweet; Check Mates; Bon Voyage; Miss Suburbia; Fifth Avenue; Kitchen Cutie; Windy Weather; Lazy Days; Black Magic; Miss American Character.*

Cricket's wardrobe is also shown in the brochure. She can wear *Hootenanny; School Days; Ship Ahoy; Windy Weather; Sugar 'n Spice.*

SEE: *Illustration 63.* (*Tressy* brochure).

Illustration 64. (*Tressy* brochure).

Illustration 63.

Illustration 64.

New Tressy (Magic Make-up Face): *Barbie®* look-alike; plastic body; poseable vinyl arms and legs with soft vinyl head; 12in (31cm); pale face and eyes so children could apply makeup; painted side-glancing eyes; turquoise eye shadow above eyes; grow hair operated by button and key; dated 1965; jointed at neck, shoulders, hips; no mold marks under wrists; high-heeled feet; 1965-1966.

The folder which came with the *New Tressy* (Magic Make-up Face) explains, "The NEW TRESSY comes with hair that grows...legs that pose...and a new Magic Make-up Face." The child was given instructions for eye and lip makeup. There were also instructions for removing makeup. There was a new *Tressy* cosmetic kit #1215 which included lipstick, eye shadow, nail polish, hair color applicator and sponges. Like other popular dolls of the period, the skin color was "natural" so that cosmetics could be applied.

MARKS: None on doll.
SEE: *Illustration 65.* (*New Tressy* brochure).
PRICE: $25-30

New Tressy Fashion Shop: For general characteristics, see *Illustration 65;* box had inset which had painted chests, wall cupboard, wallpaper as setting for the *Magic Make-up Face Doll*; clothes included were a red cotton two piece, high neck suit; a blue strapless short evening dress trimmed in white lace; and a black and white polka dot street dress with ruffles around sleeve; extra black and white shoes, black pocketbook; white nylon stockings; fashion brochure. The dress in the center is *Sugar 'n Spice.*

Tressy is a *Barbie®* look-alike.

MARKS: "Tressy//fashion shop//set & style Tressy's hair to match her hi-fashion outfits//American Character" (box); no marks on doll.
SEE: *Illustration 66.*
PRICE: $50-55

Barbie® is a registered trademark of Mattel, Inc.

Illustration 66.

Illustration 65.

Illustration 67.

Tressy Hat Shop: In *Playthings*, March 1965, American Character advertised new merchandising excitement. They introduced a new *Tressy's* Hat Shoppe. The doll on the left shows an illustration. It is similar to the *Tressy* Fashion Shop. They also made Glamour Paks and new Budget Clothes.

SEE: *Illustration 67. Playthings*, March 1965.

Illustration 68.

Cricket: Plastic body with vinyl head, arms, limbs; wired and poseable legs; 9in (23cm); side-glancing painted eyes; hair that grows; had both "high fashion" and budget clothes which originally sold for $1.50 and $2.00; 11 outfits in all. *Cricket* is *Tressy's* pre-teen sister.

Illustrations from left to right: *Kitchen Cutie, Winter Weekend, Budget Dress. Cricket* holds boxed high fashions.

MARKS: "Amer. Char.//1964" on head.

SEE: *Illustration 68. Playthings*, February 1965. Outfits left to right: *Kitchen Cutie, Winter Weekend, Budget Dress, Cricket* holding boxed high fashions.

PRICE: $25-30

Mary Make-up: Vinyl; 11½in (29cm); *Barbie*® look-alike; jointed at neck, shoulders, hips; pale face so makeup could be applied easily; poseable; white rooted hair; painted side glancing eyes; *Tressy's* best friend; wardrobe includes a satin dance dress with high-heeled shoes and bag; suspender skirt and checked top with knee socks; shirt with boots and bag; accessories included necklace, bag, sneakers, troll doll; glamour kit could be ordered which included blushing lipstick, eyebrow pencil, cosmetic sponges, nail polish, perfume; a hair coloring kit was available with blonde, red, brunette colors; doll wearing red sheath; circa 1964-1966.

MARKS: None.

SEE: *Illustration 69.* (advertisement for *Mary Make-up*). *Anne Pendleton Collection.*

PRICE: $30-35

Barbie® is a registered trademark of Mattel, Inc.

Illustration 69.

Pre-teen Tressy: Firm hollow plastic body and legs; soft vinyl head and arms; 14in (36cm); sleep eyes with real lashes; three painted eyelash lines at outer corners of eyes; feathered eyebrows; pretty cream color flesh tone; grow hair like *Tressy*; mechanism through center of body which operates the grow hair in top of head; 3rd and 4th fingers molded together and slightly curled; clothes not original but from printed pattern of period; looks like *Betsy McCall*®; jointed at neck, shoulders, legs; 1963.

MARKS: "Am. Char. 63®" (head).

SEE: *Illustration 70.* (from *Tressy* brochure).
   Illustration 71. (doll).

PRICE: $95-115 and up (rare doll).

Betsy McCall® is a registered trademark of the McCall Corp.

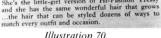

Illustration 70.

Illustration 71.

Popi: Plastic; *Barbie®* look-alike; 12in (31cm); high-heeled fashion doll; came in kit with vinyl clothes which could be cut and used to dress the doll with no sewing; circa 1961-1962.

The doll came apart in three places. Plastic pegs were used to connect the doll. The design of the clothes was amazing. The clothes were stamped on vinyl. The dress was first cut out with scissors. There was no sewing. By taking apart the doll and following the directions on the vinyl, the doll could be dressed. The clothes hooked under, over, on and through the body parts and pegs.

> **MARKS:** None on doll; "Fashion Kit//Popi//the//pop-apart//fashion model//with//3 separate wigs" (box).
> **SEE:** *Illustration 72.* (doll with vinyl dress, kits and original box).
> > *Illustration 73.* (undressed doll with cut out clothes).
> **PRICE:** $30 (doll in box)
> $10 (costume packet)

Barbie® is a registered trademark of Mattel, Inc.

Illustration 72.

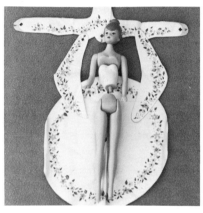

Illustration 73.

Whimsies: One-piece stuffed vinyl body with molded head; 21in (53cm); molded painted eyes; closed smiling mouth.

The Whimsey series includes: *Polly the Lolly; The Tiny Whimsies; Miss Take; Girl Devil; Zack the Sack; Monk or Friar; Simon the Degree; Zero the Hero; Dixie the Pixie; Lena the Cleaner; Fanny* (Angel); *Susie the Snoozie; Hedda Get Bedda; Raggie Strong Man; Bessie the Bashful Bride; Wheeler the Dealer; Tillie the Talker.*

> **MARKS:** "Whimsie//Amer. Doll & Toy Co." (head).
> **SEE:** *Illustration 74. Playthings,* June 1960.
> **PRICE:** $90-100

Illustration 74.

Whimsies: For general characteristics, see *Illustration 74;* New for 1961:
1. *Trixie the Pixie* dressed like the devil
2. *Fanny the Flapper*
3. *Samson the Strong*
4. *Bessie the Bashful Bride*
>   **SEE:** *Illustration 75. Toys and Novelties*, March 1961.
>   **PRICE:** $90-100

Caroline Kennedy Look-alike: Plastic body and soft vinyl head; 14in (36cm); rooted blonde hair in a soft "pageboy" hairdo in back of head; imitates both hair and face of Alexander's *Caroline*®; three painted eyelashes on side of each eye; clothes not original; 1965.
>   **MARKS:** "AME. Char. Inc.//19c65"
>   **SEE:** *Illustration 76. Inga Tomoletz Collection.*
>   **PRICE:** $30-35 (in original clothes)

Caroline® is a registered trademark of the Alexander Doll Co., Inc.

Illustration 75.   *Illustration 76.*

Illustration 77.

Blue Ribbon Doll: Hollow plastic body and legs; soft vinyl arms and head; 13in (33cm); sleep eyes with real lashes; three painted lines at outer corners of eyes; black pupiless sleep, side-glancing eyes; rooted curly hair; topknot of hair at top of head but no "growing" mechanism; jointed at neck, shoulders, hips; individual fingers; pouty-type mouth and expression on face; all original clothes; blue and white plaid dress with white collar and felt cutout bow: lace trim to make dress the popular "trapeze" style of the era; 1965.

    MARKS: "AM. CHAR. INC.// 1965" (head); "A Blue Ribbon Doll//American Character// Style No. 1506" (box).

    SEE: *Illustration 77.*

    PRICE: $25-30

Little Miss Echo: Plastic body, soft vinyl head; 30in (76cm); jointed at neck, shoulders, hips; three transistor circuit with continuous magnetic tape; repeats the child's words for almost half a minute; several hair and costume models; open-mouth; molded tongue; two upper teeth; ornate red lever for operation of mechanism on chest; unusual green eyes; advertised in Alden's Christmas catalog; 1964.

    MARKS: None

    SEE: *Illustration 78. Playthings*, June 1962.

        Illustration 79. (close-up of face showing red lever). *Inga Tomoletz Collection.*

PRICE: $140-150

Illustration 78.

Illustration 79.

Illustration 80.

Toodles with Peek-a-Boo Eyes: Plastic body, soft vinyl head; 25in (64cm); open-mouth with four upper teeth and two lower teeth; molded tongue; eyes follow person without moving; feathered eyebrows; not original clothes; 1960.

Featured on Shari Lewis NBC-TV network show sponsored by American Doll and Toy Company.

MARKS: "American Character//19c60" (head).

SEE: *Illustration 80. Inga Tomoletz Collection.*

PRICE: $125-140 (with original clothes).

DOLLS NOT PHOTOGRAPHED

Tiny Whimsies: All vinyl; 6in (15cm); painted eyes; closed-mouth; assorted hair and clothes; includes: *Pixie, Swinger, Granny, Minnie Mod, Junk N, GoGo*; circa 1961.

MARKS: "Made in Hong Kong" (head); "Whimsies//American Character, Inc" (box).

Arranbee Doll Company

The registered trademarks, the trademarks and the copyrights appearing in italics within this chapter belong to Arranbee Doll Company, unless otherwise noted.

About 1957 the Arranbee Doll Company was purchased by the Vogue Doll Company and Arranbee became a part of Vogue. Some of the all-vinyl and hard plastic and vinyl Angel dolls were marketed by the Arranbee division of Vogue. The catalog reprinted in this section will help with the identification of some of these dolls after the merger.

Arranbee's popular 11in (28cm) *Littlest Angel* doll was used by Vogue in 1959 for their *Li'l Imp®*. (See *Illustration 424*.) Both doll were marked "R & B" on the back of their heads. Both dolls were walking dolls with a hard plastic body with jointed knees and a vinyl head. Both dolls and their wardrobes had boxes with the name of the original company. The clothes could be used for either doll.

Many of the other Angel dolls found in this catalog have a Vogue mark. Some of them are pictured in the Vogue section of this book. (See *Illustration 427*.)

Coty® Girl Doll: Rigid vinyl body, soft vinyl head; 10½in (27cm); high heeled; swivel waist; jointed at neck, shoulders, hips, waist; face uses Circle P mold (see page 184); body similar to *Little Miss Revlon®* doll; blue sleep eyes; curved brown eyebrows; painted red lips, finger and toenails; rooted thick long blonde hair; other hair colors included brunette and tosca; arm tag front reads, "Coty Girl Doll//I am all vinyl and can be washed from head to toe. My washable hair is rooted just like real growing hair;" arm tag on back reads, "It's easy and so much fun to give me a new hair-do. Moisten the hair lightly with water-Set hair in curlers. When hair is dry remove curlers. Very simple indeed;" side of her box reads, "Hello I'm the new *Coty Girl Doll*. Out of the TV Screen — into your home to give you hours of pleasure. Keep me glamorous in my many beautiful costumes for every occasion;" doll was used to advertise and promote Coty® cosmetics and beauty supplies; high quality doll with glamorous, well-made fashion clothes that came with many accessories; outfits could be purchased separately and came boxed in several styles of boxes; doll wearing original outfit; black felt hat; black satin cocktail dress with lace overskirt; bodice trimmed in black lace; pearl necklace and earrings; stockings; black sandals with clear high heels; this outfit alone was priced at $5.00; circa 1958.

Not all dolls marked with Ⓟ or that use this mold mark are *Coty®* dolls. *Coty®* dolls have an excellent quality, thick hair, and like *Miss Revlon®*, the hair could be washed and set. Many Ⓟ dolls have rough hair that does not set well.

Li'l Imp® is a registered trademark of Vogue Dolls, Inc.
Coty® is a registered trademark of Coty Div. Pfizer.
Revlon® is a registered trademark of Revlon, Inc.

MARKS: None but horizontal line found on Circle P molds (see *Illustration 331*), some *Coty*® dolls marked " Ⓟ " (back of head).

SEE: *Illustration 81.*

PRICE: $70-85+ (doll and box)
$45-65+ (doll)
$20-30 (boxed outfit)

Illustration 81.

Illustration 82.

Coty*® *Girl Doll Brochure: Top: introduction to the *Coty*® doll.
Bottom:
1. *Print Percale Dress*
2. *Cowl Neck Dress*
3. *Rain Outfit*; circa 1958
MARKS: None
SEE: *Illustration 83. Marybeth Manchook Collection.*
PRICE: $20-25+ (boxed outfits)

Coty*® *Girl Doll: See color page 9; original negligee outfit; pink nylon nightgown trimmed with white lace; blue nylon robe with flocked pink and white flowers; blue high-heeled shoes; circa 1958.
MARKS: None
SEE: *Illustration 82.*
PRICE: $45-65+ (doll)
$20+ (boxed outfit)

Illustration 83.

Coty*® *Girl Doll Brochure:
Top:
1. *Negligee Outfit*
2. *Dress and Wool Shrug*
3. *Gingham Check Dress*
Bottom:
1. *Blue Stripe Dress*
2. *Swim Suit and Cape*
3. *Cocktail Party Dress*; circa 1958
MARKS: None
SEE: *Illustration 84. Marybeth Manchook Collection.*
PRICE: $20-25 (boxed outfits)

Illustration 84.

Coty® is a registered trademark of Coty Div. Pfizer.

Coty® Girl Doll Brochure:
Top:
  1. *Tailored Suit and Blouse*
  2. *Square Dancer*
  3. *Toreador*
Middle:
  1. *Denim Play Outfit*
  2. *Velvet Wrap and Formal*
  3. *Coat, Hat and Muff*
Bottom:
  1. *Tulle Formal*
  2. *Bride Outfit*; circa 1958
MARKS: None
SEE: *Illustration 85. Marybeth Manchook Collection.*
PRICE: $25-30 (boxed outfits)

Coty® is a registered trademark of Coty Div. Pfizer.

Illustration 85.

Illustration 86.

Littlest Angel: Hard plastic body and soft vinyl head; 11in (28cm); jointed at neck, shoulders, hips, knees; rooted hair; sleep eyes; blonde, brunette, tosca Dutch-cut type hair; circa 1957-59.

This page shows a ten-piece wardrobe plus the basic doll dressed in pants, shoes and socks. There is also a trunk set with some of the clothes. This is a very late *Littlest Angel* doll.
  MARKS: "R & B" (head)
  SEE: *Illustration 86. Arranbee Doll Company catalog.*
  PRICE: $50-75+ (depending on outfit)

Illustration 87.

My Angel: All vinyl; 17in (43cm); rooted hair arranged in Dutch bob; fully jointed; sleep eyes; circa 1957-59.
  SEE: *Illustration 87* (top row). *Arranbee Doll Company catalog.*
  PRICE: $55-75 (depending on outfit)

My Angel: Polyethylene body and legs; soft vinyl arms and head; 26in (66cm); rooted side-part bob; fully jointed; sleep eyes, circa 1957-59.

> **SEE:** *Illustration 87* (middle and bottom row). *Arranbee Doll Company catalog.*
>
> **PRICE:** $65-80

My Angel Walking Doll: Polyethylene body and legs; soft vinyl arms and head; 30in (76cm); walking mechanism; fully jointed; sleep eyes; 1957-59.

> **SEE:** *Illustration 88. Arranbee Doll Company catalog.*
>
> **PRICE:** $80-90

Illustration 87.

Illustration 88.

Illustration 89.

My Angel Walking Doll: Polyethylene body and legs; soft vinyl arms and head; 36in (91cm); shaggy Dutch bob rooted hair; fully jointed; sleep eyes; walking mechanism; circa 1957-59.

In 1960 this doll was used for a *Walking Ginny®* doll which came with an 8in (20cm) *Ginny®* doll in an identical outfit.

> **PRICE:** $100-135 (doll alone; no *Ginny®* 8in [20cm])
>
> **SEE:** *Illustration 89.*

Angel: All vinyl body and head; 17in (43cm) and 21in (53cm); side-part bob hair; fully jointed; sleep eyes; circa 1957-1959.

> **SEE:** *Illustration 90. Arranbee Doll Company catalog,* see page 243.
>
> **PRICE:** $55-70 (depending on outfit)

Walking Ginny® and *Ginny®* are registered trademarks of Vogue Dolls, Inc.

Arrow

The registered trademarks, the trademarks and the copyrights appearing in italics within this chapter belong to Arrow.

Doll in Orange Dress: (doll on left); rigid vinyl body; soft vinyl head; 24in (61cm); reddish rooted hair; real lashes on sleep eyes; three eyelashes painted on the side of each eye; closed-mouth; jointed at neck, shoulders, hips; swivel waist; high heeled, ⅄ on backside; individual fingers; red fingernails and toenails; older teenage figure; orange satin dress with large darker orange bow at waist; 1958.

Doll on the right is a Deluxe Premium Doll by Deluxe Toy Co. See page 87 for close-up of faces. They are exactly the same doll except for the arrow mark. Their dresses are the same, but with different colors. They were often sold in grocery stores.

MARKS: A diamond with an arrow inside; 21 next to diamond (doll on left). A smaller size doll with the same dress had an "A" on its back.
SEE: *Illustration 91.*
PRICE: $25-30 (doll on left)
$35-40 (doll on right in mint condition)

Beehler Arts, Ltd.

The registered trademarks, the trademarks and the copyrights appearing in italics within this chapter belong to Beehler Arts, Ltd.

High Heel Doll: Rigid vinyl body and legs; soft vinyl head and arms; 10½in (27cm); jointed only at head and shoulders; one-piece body and legs; rooted blonde coarse hair; poorer quality doll than others of this type and size; the head is an unmarked Circle P mold, see page 184, blue sleep eyes; three very slanted painted lashes at side of each eye; 3rd and 4th fingers molded together; high-heeled; blue felt bathing suit with a black felt belt; circa 1959.

MARKS: None on doll, but head has mold line of the Circle P type, see page 184.
SEE: *Illustration 92.*
PRICE: $15

Illustration 91. (Arrow)

Illustration 92. (Beehler Arts)

Belle Doll and Toy Corp.

The registered trademarks, the trademarks and the copyrights appearing in italics within this chapter belong to Belle Doll and Toy Corp., unless otherwise noted.

Illustration 93.

Bride: Very nice rigid vinyl body and soft vinyl head; 15in (38cm); blonde rooted hair; pierced ears with pearl earrings; sleep eyes with real lashes; painted eyelashes under eyes; individual fingers; jointed at neck, shoulders and hips; high-heeled feet; Y on backside; plastic disk between joints at hips; satin wedding dress with flocked net overlay; crinoline and satin petticoats; black girdle with garters which hold up nylon stockings; pearl tiara holds net veil with lace trim; circa 1957.

> **MARKS:** "15 BAL HH" (back just below waist)
> **SEE:** *Illustration 93.*
> **PRICE:** $40-50

Margie: Hard plastic body with vinyl face; 20in (51cm); jointed at neck, shoulders and hips; rooted hair; sleep eyes with lashes; high heeled; dark blue satin dress with pink dots; black net stockings and gloves; small pink satin hat; circa 1957-59.

> This is a *Cissy*®-type doll.
> **MARKS:** No marks on doll; "Margie//the Teenage Doll" (box)
> **SEE:** *Illustration 94. Marybeth Manchook Collection.*
> **PRICE:** $45-50

Cissy® is a registered trademark of the Alexander Doll Co., Inc.

Illustration 94.

DOLLS NOT PHOTOGRAPHED

Little Miss Margie: Rigid vinyl; 10in (25cm); jointed at neck, shoulders, waist, hip; sleep blue eyes; high-heeled feet; 1957-1958.

> **MARKS:** "Ⓟ" (head); "Belle Doll and Toy Corp." (box)

Bonomi (Italy)

The registered trademarks, the trademarks and the copyrights appearing in italics within this chapter belong to Bonomi.

In Italy, as well as the United States, dolls were well dressed and were considered "chic." Italian dolls have large deep eyes and a look of their own people. Sears advertised so aptly, "Have you ever seen outfits so smartly styled, so beautifully detailed, so definitely continental in fashion?"

Girl: See *Illustration 97* for general description.

Doll on left; 15in (38cm); dressed in black taffeta dress accented in white; box-pleated skirt; long puffed sleeves; sash; pettislip; knit panties and socks.

Doll on right: dressed in pink cotton velveteen dress; trimmed in misty lace; dickey front; full bouffant skirt; pettislip; knit panties and socks; 1963.

SEE: *Illustration 95. Sears catalog, 1963. Mary Elizabeth Poole Collection.*

Illustration 95.   *Illustration 96.*

Wardrobe for Dolls from Italy: Vinyl; 15in (38cm); for general characteristics, see *Illustration 97; from left to right:*

1. Red, white, black plaid dress with fringed scarf tie and hem-placed pockets.
2. Resort set: yellow cotton Capri pants; white and vari-colored jacket and hat.
3. Beach set: one-piece red playsuit; hooded white and red terry jacket.
4. Sweater set: knit blue and white cardigan; white pleated skirt.
5. Rain wear: white, brown, tan checked pants; white knit shirt; yellow plastic rain cape.
6. Coat: royal blue lined wool coat with princess lines; chin-tie hat; rayon print dress.
7. Ball gown: blue nylon formal gown; lacy overlay caught in scallops.
8. Pajamas: Capri length cotton; sleeveless top; lace trimmed; both in white, red, green print.

SEE: *Illustration 96. Sears catalog, 1963. Mary Elizabeth Poole Collection.*

Illustration 97.

Girl: Vinyl body and soft vinyl head; hard plastic legs; 15in (38cm); rooted hair in long flip style; sleep eyes; jointed at neck, shoulders, hips; high color fashion type; clothes not original; 1963.

MARKS: "MC (in square)//c 1963//736//Made in Italy"

SEE: *Illustration 97. Ester Borgis Collection.*

PRICE: $35-40

Brevete GeGe of France

The registered trademarks, the trademarks and the copyrights appearing in italics within this chapter belong to Brevete S.G.D.G.

Illustration 98.

SEE: *Illustration 99.*

From left to right: *Trousseau Alaska; Trousseau Ala Page; Trousseau Opera; Trousseau Courmayeur; Trousseau Drugstore; Short Skirt and Blouse; Trousseau Frivolite; Trousseau Balmoral; Trousseau Reve; Trousseau Pre-Catelan.*

GeGe: Hard French vinyl body and soft vinyl arms and head; 21in (53cm); beautiful silver blonde rooted hair; sleep eyes with real lashes and three painted lashes at corners of eyes; closed-mouth; individual fingers on left hand; four molded fingers on right hand; jointed at neck, shoulders, waist, hips; pink lips; green, turquoise, yellow, white pants and turtle neck top; mock white lamb's wool coat and hat; both coat and hat have metal "GeGe" medallion sewn on; circa 1965+.

MARKS: "GeGe//MC5"(head); "M5 Made in France" (body); "Dolly//GeGe//Taille Articulee//Brevete S.G.D.G." (box)

SEE: *Illustration 98* (doll and box).

PRICE: $45-70 (depending on outfit)

Illustration 99.

Brookglad Corp.

The registered trademarks, the trademarks and the copyrights appearing in italics within this chapter belong to Brookglad Corp.

Poor Pitiful Pearl: Soft vinyl; 18in (46cm); can sit, stand, bend, kneel; teaches good grooming habits to children who care for her; sorrowful expression on face; long rooted Saran hair; advertised on Dave Garroway TV show; 1957.

The very pliable vinyl has now hardened. It cracks easily when moved out of its permanent form.

SEE: Also Horsman, page 190.
SEE: Also Gladtoy, page 112.
MARKS: "Gladtoy" (head)
PRICE: $35-45

Citro

The registered trademarks, the trademarks and the copyrights appearing in italics within this chapter belong to Citro, unless otherwise noted.

Polly Pond's® Beauty Doll: Stuffed vinyl on piece body; soft vinyl head; 24in (61cm); jointed at neck only; legs wired so they pose; very beautiful blonde doll with lovely complexion; ponytail, earrings, clothes all original; taffeta dress; white nylon blouse; stockings with seam; black high heeled shoes; circa 1956. She was an advertising doll and came with a Pond's Beauty Kit consisting of Pond's Cold Cream, Pond's Tissues, lipstick, Angel Skin Hand and Body Lotion.

> **MARKS:** "4595" under hair on upper head; round circle on back of neck; "Polly Pond's Beauty Kit//Polly Pond's Beauty Doll" on box.
> **SEE:** *Illustration 102.*
> **PRICE:** $35-50

Pond's® is a registered trademark of Chesebrough Pond's Inc.

Illustration 102.

Commonwealth Corp.

The registered trademarks, the trademarks and the copyrights appearing in italics within this chapter belong to Commonwealth Corp.

Illustration 104.

Dress-Me Dolls: In March 1960 Commonwealth advertised an 8in (20cm) adult vinyl doll with rooted hair and high-heeled shoes, Style D-83. They also advertised a 10in (25cm) adult vinyl doll with rooted hair and a swivel waist and high-heel shoes, Style D-101. Another doll was a 10in (25cm) adult doll with high heels and a mohair wig, Style D-102.

By this time the company had added the entire "doll bodies" line to their own and the Lingerie Lou logo (Doll Bodies) was in one corner of the page.

MARKS: Possible W1 on head; or none.

SEE: *Illustration 104. Playthings,* March 1960.

Cosmopolitan Toy & Doll Corporation

The registered trademarks, the trademarks and the copyrights appearing in italics within this chapter belong to Cosmopolitan Toy & Doll Corporation, unless otherwise noted.

Cosmopolitan was an established company known for their hard plastic *Ginger* doll, a *Ginny®* competitor. They were one of the first doll companies to sell high-heeled dolls starting in 1957 with a medium-heeled *Ginger* walking doll with Cha Cha heels. In 1957 a high-heeled teen, *Miss Ginger*, was added to their line followed by a smaller high-heeled doll, *Little Miss Ginger*. Fashionable clothes and accessories could be purchased separately. Their famous *Little Miss Ginger* chorus line was used to advertise their products on television from October 15th until Christmas, 1958.

SEE: *Illustration 105. Toys and Novelties,* August, 1958.

Ginny® is a registered trademark of Vogue Dolls, Inc.

Illustration 105.   *Illustration 106.*

Ginger Grows Up with Cha Cha Heel: Hard plastic with vinyl head; 8in (20cm); head turning walking doll; sleep eyes with no eyelashes; jointed at neck, arms, hips; medium heels (see Identification Guide, *Hard Plastic Dolls*, pages 81 and 266N; short heavy thighs; checked dress with straw hat; vinyl head is superior to most other *Ginger* vinyl heads; 1957.

She can wear *Ginger's* clothes.

MARKS: "Ginger" (bottom of feet); "Ginger" (bottom of Cha Cha shoes)
SEE: *Illustration 106. Playthings*, March 1957.
PRICE: $30-40+ (rare)

Illustration 107.

Miss Ginger: 10½in (27cm); slim teen-age sister to *Ginger* with high-heeled feet; doll introduced in *Playthings*, March 1957; added feature was the matching *Ginger* and *Miss Ginger* clothes.

    MARKS: "GINGER" (head)
    SEE: *Illustration 107.*
    PRICE: $110-125 (pair)

Illustration 108. *Illustration 109.*

Miss Gingers (Left): rigid vinyl body, soft vinyl head; 10½in (27cm); long blonde rooted hair with the top gathered into a ponytail; blue sleep eyes; very red lips; jointed at neck, shoulders, waist, legs; white pearl earrings; red fingernails; dressed tagged; black and white striped cotton dress with a red vest, hat, shoes; white nylon slip trimmed with lace; nylon stockings; well made clothes. (Right): hard plastic body, soft vinyl head; 10½in (27cm); long blonde rooted hair; blue sleep eyes; red lips; jointed at neck, shoulders, legs; white formal with blue-green print; green underskirt; black bows; circa 1958.

    MARKS: "GINGER" (head); both dresses tagged "Fashions for Ginger"
    SEE: *Illustration 108.*
    PRICE: $50-60 (doll on right)
              $40-50 (doll on left)

Miss Gingers (Left): hard plastic body, soft vinyl head; 10½in (27cm); brown hair; blue sleep eyes; red lips and fingernails; 3rd and 4th fingers molded; high heeled; red corduroy skirt and red checked blouse; jointed at neck, legs, shoulders; (Right): rigid vinyl body, soft vinyl head; 10½in (27cm); long blonde hair; pearl earrings; blue sleep eyes; red lips and fingernails; high heeled; jointed at waist, neck, shoulders, legs; red, black, gray, white plaid cotton dress; straw hat trimmed with black lace; circa 1958.

    MARKS: "GINGER" (head); no marks on either body; clothes tagged "Ginger"
    SEE: *Illustration 109.*
    PRICE: $35-45 (doll on left)
              $40-50 (doll on right)

Miss Ginger: For doll description see *Illustrations 108* and *109*; all clothes are tagged, "Fashions for Ginger/Cosmopolitan Doll & Toy Corp./Richmond Hill, N.Y./R Trade Mark:" (Left): pink nylon formal with a pink nylon lace overdress; (Middle): nurse outfit with a blue cotton dress and white apron and hat; (Right): pink gingham cotton dress trimmed with white lace with pink straw bonnet; circa 1958.

    MARKS: "GINGER" (head)
    SEE: *Illustration 110.*
    PRICE: $40-50 (middle doll)
              $35-40 (dolls on left and right)

Illustration 110.

Illustration 111.

Illustration 112.

Miss Ginger Brochure: This is part of a *Ginger* brochure. Each outfit could be purchased for both *Miss Ginger* and her little sister, *Ginger*. However, only the *Miss Ginger* outfit is shown because the *Ginger* outfit was pictured in the first part of the brochure. Prices were given for the outfit and doll or the outfit alone.

MARKS: "GINGER" (head)

SEE: *Illustration 111.*

     Illustration 112.

PRICE: $20-30 (boxed outfit)

Illustration 113.

Little Miss Ginger: Rigid vinyl body and soft vinyl head; 8in (20cm); slim doll; rooted hair; high heeled; jointed at neck, shoulders, legs; blue sleep eyes with molded lashes; well proportioned mature body; very red lips, fingernails, toes; 3rd and 4th fingernails molded together; advertisement states, "Yours on velvet / *Little Miss Ginger* / The most precious doll in the world / The only all vinyl eight inch slim doll / Wrapped in a dazzling 'package' that includes full color page advertising in Life Magazine;" 1958.

MARKS: "GINGER" (head)
SEE: *Illustration 113 Playthings*, January 1958.

Little Miss Ginger: For doll description, see *Illustration 113;* Left: original clothes; red cotton dress with white teardrops; white organdy collar; skirt trimmed with white lace; red net hat with white flowers; stockings; white shoes; matching white purse; tagged dress; Right: doll is *Miss Nancy Ann*; see page 177; it closely resembles *Little Miss Ginger*; nurse outfit; white starched cotton dress, white organdy apron; matching white hat with red cross; tagged dress.

MARKS: "GINGER" (left); no marks (right).
SEE: *Illustration 114.*
PRICE: $45-50

Illustration 114.

Ginger with Cha Cha Heels and Little Miss Ginger: For general characteristics of *Little Miss Ginger*, see *Illustration 113.*

MARKS: See *Illustration 113.*
SEE: *Illustration 115.*
PRICE: $30-40+ (*Cha Cha* rare)
$30 (*Little Miss Ginger,* right)

Illustration 115.

Debbie Toy Company

The registered trademarks, the trademarks and the copyrights appearing in italics within this chapter belong to Debbie Toy Company, unless otherwise noted.

In mid 1959 the Debbie Toy Company was founded by John Landers, Shelley Greenburg and William Cohen. Landers was the inventor of the *Ballerina®* doll manufactured by Valentine Dolls, Inc. This was an innovative company which manufactured their own dolls and also produced other products such as strollers, carriages, teeter chairs and car beds.

When the 32in (81cm) *Debbie* was introduced, 4000 dozen were ordered in four days. One week later all production for the year had been sold.

Ballerina® is a registered trademark of Valentine Dolls, Inc.

Debbie Toy sells 1,000 dozen dolls per day

The new thirty-two inch walker doll by Debbie Toy, 200 Fifth ave., New York, is a striking example of the creativity exhibited by a newly-founded firm in producing a doll which excited buyers. On first showing the doll produced enthusiastic buyer response to the tune of 4,000 dozen dolls ordered in four days. One week later all production for the year had been sold!

Such a tremendous response reflects on the management of a firm that has, in one year, carved itself a prominent niche in the toy industry. The men responsible for this success are the three partners of the Debby Toy firm.

In mid 1959 three men established Debbie Toy, John Landers, Shelley Greenburg and William Cohen.

John Landers, president of the year-old firm, spent seven years with Martins in Brooklyn. Landers was the inventor of the Ballerina doll manufactured by Valentine Doll; with Valentine Landers was for

FOUR STYLES of this 32" doll are available in red, blonde, brunette or brown sculptured pixie hair do. Doll will retail at approximately $8.95. Fully dressed doll comes in a beautifully flocked dress of nylon with a fancy lace trimmed slip, patent leather shoes, socks and painted to match the dress and slip.

TOYS and NOVELTIES—*December, 1960*

Illustration 116.

Debbie Doll stands 11½" tall, made of all vinyl with rooted hair. Comes complete with bathing suits, high heels, in addition to four other costumes. Packaged on heavy printed card. $2.98 retail. Debbie Toy, 200 Fifth ave., NYC.

Illustration 117.

Debbie Walker: Vinyl; 32in (81cm); available in red, blonde, brunette, brown sculptured hair; character face; dressed in flocked nylon dress with fancy lace-trimmed slip; patent leather shoes; socks.
SEE: *Illustration 116. Toys and Novelties*, December 1960.
PRICE: $85-95

Debbie Doll: Vinyl *Barbie®* look-alike; 11½in (29cm); rooted hair; high-heel fashion doll; striped bathing suit; came with four other costumes; packaged on heavy printed card; 1962.
MARKS: Some dolls have a "v" on the neck
SEE: *Illustration 117. Toys and Novelties*, March 1962.
PRICE: $15-20

Barbie® is a registered trademark of Mattel, Inc.

Deluxe Reading

The registered trademarks, the trademarks and the copyrights appearing in italics within this chapter belong to Deluxe Reading.

This company produced many dolls for the mass market during the 1957 to 1965 period. Some of these dolls were premiums or sold at food markets only. They were inexpensive, bright, cheerful, and many young collectors remember going to the grocery stores and "begging" their mother to buy whatever was necessary to obtain one of the lovely dolls on the top shelf as a premium.

The dolls by Deluxe Reading were marketed under several names including Deluxe Reading, Deluxe Topper, Topper Corp., Topper Toys, Deluxe Toy Creations and Deluxe Premium Corporation. Other companies such as Arrow used the same dolls at times. Occasionally, the costumes were the same. (See *Illustration 91.*)

Many different markings were used by Deluxe Reading for their diverse lines of dolls. These included the names of their various companies above. Other markings included "14R" and "AE" followed by a number.

Illustration 118.

Candy Fashion: Vinyl with softer vinyl head; 20in (51cm); jointed at neck, shoulders, elbows, hips, knees; rooted Saran hair; high heels; came with four completely matched ensembles; sold only at food markets at $12.98; 1962.

MARKS: "21 HH//K74"(head); other marks seen on *Candy* doll include "A1 HH K92" and "A1 HH K70"

SEE: *Illustration 118* (doll inside of box). *Marybeth Manchook Collection.*

PRICE: $50-60

Candy Fashion 4 Season Wardrobe (description):
1. Autumn Days — blue suit with red accents on collar of pocket; blue short sleeve blouse; red turned-up sailor hat trimmed in blue; red high-heeled shoes; red beaded necklace; red model's box.
2. Spring Fancy — green dress trimmed in white at collar and cuffs; pert bow at waistline; softly turned collar that plunges to deep points at the rear; green hat trimmed with white; black patent leather shoes; handbag.
3. Capri — three-piece violet bathing ensemble including wrap-around skirt, jacket; one-piece bathing suit; beach shoes; sunglasses; straw hat; resort necklace.
4. Sophisticate — pink chiffon evening gown with sequin trim; matching stole; pink taffeta underskirt; drop earrings; sweetheart necklace; evening shoes; evening bag.

Girl in Pink Hat: Rigid vinyl body; soft vinyl head; 24in (61cm); reddish rooted hair; sleep eyes with real lashes; three eyelashes painted on the side of each eye; closed-mouth; jointed at neck, shoulders, hips; swivel waist; high heels; Y on backside; individual fingers; red fingernails and toenails; older teenage figure; pink satin dress with large rose bow at waist and large rose hat; all original; 1958.

Doll on left is an Arrow doll. See *Illustration 91.* Doll on right is a Deluxe doll.

> **MARKS:** None on body; "Copyright 1958 Deluxe Premium Corp. Newark 4, N.J." (side of box)
> **SEE:** *Illustration 119. Marybeth Manchook Collection.*
> **PRICE:** $35-40

Illustration 119.

Betty the Beautiful Bride: Stuffed vinyl body, soft vinyl head; 29in (74cm); flexible arms and legs; washable rooted hair; sleep eyes with lashes; high-heeled feet; red painted fingernails but not toenails; beautiful bride dress of silver-shot net over white satin with rows of ruffles on the skirt; tiara-type veil; unusual rhinestone buckles on high-heel shoes; all original; came with simulated pearl collarette, bridal bouquet, wall plaque; Bing Crosby's record of "Because." Circa 1957-59.

> **MARKS:** "86" (back of doll); "Betty the Beautiful Bride, wearing the most exquisite Bridal Gown ever designed// Copyright Deluxe Premium Corp. Newark 4, N.J." (box)
> **SEE:** *Illustration 120* (doll in box). *Jean Hall Collection.*
> **PRICE:** $65-75

Illustration 120.

Bride: Stuffed vinyl; 25in (64cm); high heeled; thin waisted; sleep eyes with painted eye highlights in corner of eyes; painted eyebrows; jointed at neck only; ruffled bridal gown; gray fur stole; seamed nylons; white hat; 1957-58.

> **MARKS:** "VH-25-19" (heel and bottom of foot); "25/1-H7" (side of box)
> **SEE:** *Illustration 121. Sharlene Doyle Collection.*
> **PRICE:** $35-50

Illustration 121.

Bride: Rigid vinyl with soft vinyl head; 24in (61cm); jointed at neck, shoulders, hips, sleep eyes with lashes; painted lashes under eyes; rooted blonde hair; Y on seat; high-heeled; satin dress with net and lace overskirt; tiara holds net veil; circa 1957-60.

> **MARKS:** "SG"
> **SEE:** *Illustration 122. Marybeth Manchook Collection.*
> **PRICE:** $25-50

Illustration 122.

Illustration 123.

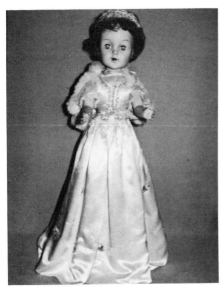

Princess: Rigid vinyl with soft vinyl head; 24in (61cm); jointed at neck, shoulders, hips; sleep eyes with lashes; painted lashes under eyes; rooted tosca hair; Y on seat; high-heeled; jeweled crown; unusually beautiful satin dress trimmed with braid and jewels; circa 1957-60.

> **MARKS:** None
> **SEE:** *Illustration 123. Marybeth Manchook Collection.*
> **PRICE:** $25-30

Bride: Rigid vinyl with soft vinyl head; 24in (61cm); jointed at neck, shoulders, hips; sleep eyes with lashes; high heeled; beautiful lace dress with rows of ruffles which is similar to Deluxe Reading's *Betty Bride* (see *Illustration 120*); circa early 1960s.

This is probably one of the Deluxe Reading or Arrow-type dolls. They are known to have used similar numbers as marks.

> **MARKS:** "155" (head)
> **SEE:** *Illustration 124. Marybeth Manchook Collection.*
> **PRICE:** $25-30

Illustration 124.

Penny Brite was issued in 1963 as part of the Topper Line of Deluxe Reading. The first models had straight legs.

In 1964 *Penny* was introduced at the New York Toy Fair with elaborate new outfits and accessories. The brochure in the box with the 1964 doll says, "Penny Brite is the adorable new doll with more realism in extra-added play features than ever before...bending arms and legs and new turning head... dressed in lovely basic dress and shoes...pose her in any position...8in (20cm) tall...rooted hair...comes in elegantly engraved wardrobe carrying case...5 play sets-each with own dress...six additional outfits are sold separately."

Penny Brite: Vinyl; poseable arms and legs; 8in (20cm); side-glancing eyes; rooted hair; pleated embroidered red and white dress; packed in a wardrobe carry case; 1964.

Penny came with many rooms and accessories. Seen in the photograph is her "Travel Set" which included a car, hat, coat and luggage. Also seen is the "Beauty Parlor." This included a hair dryer, beauty parlor chair which tilts forward and backward, sink, stool, mirror and beauty parlor smock.

MARKS: Poseable leg model marked: "A-9//110//Deluxe Reading Corp. c.1963" (head) "Deluxe Reading Corp.//Elizabeth N.J. Pat. Pending" (back)
SEE: *Illustration 125. Penny Brite Brochure.*
PRICE: $12-15 (in box)

Illustration 125.

Penny Brite Wardrobe top to bottom:

1. *Winter Princess* — black stretch pants; white knit sweater and hat; white ice skates; hanger; Topper Toys booklet.
2. *Chit Chat* — black velvet pants; white printed top with "Chit Chat" embroidered on it; black bow in hair; red shoes; red telephone; date book; hanger; Topper Toys booklet.
3. *Sun and Fun* — red checked bathing suit; terry cloth hooded robe trimmed in red binding; straw colored sandals; beach towel stitched in red; glasses; plastic ball; hanger; Topper Toys booklet.
   SEE: *Illustration 126. Playthings*, March 1964.

Penny Brite Rooms and Accessories:

1. Kitchen Dinette — dish cabinet and sink, dishes, pans, rinse tray; dinette table and chairs, Lazy Susan, glasses; dress and apron.
2. School Room — desk and chair; blackboard and easel with chalk and eraser; briefcase with pen and book; two-piece school dress.

3. Bedroom Set bed with canopy; matching bedspread; pillow; ruffled skirt; mirror and two lamps; dresser set; two-piece pajama set.

SEE: *Illustration 127. Playthings*, March 1964.
Illustration 128. Playthings, March 1964.
Illustration 129. Playthings. March 1964.

Illustration 126.

Illustration 128.

Illustration 127.

Illustration 129.

DOLLS NOT PHOTOGRAPHED

Nancy Nurse: 21in (53cm); talks while operating on batteries; circa 1963.
MARKS: "6//19C63//Deluxe Reading" (head)

Doll Bodies Company

The registered trademarks, the trademarks and the copyrights appearing in italics within this chapter belong to Doll Bodies Company.

Doll Bodies was a company that made parts and completed dolls for many other companies. They also marketed a line of dolls themselves.

SEE: *Illustration 130. Playthings*, February 1959.

Lu-Ann: Hard plastic with soft vinyl arms and head; 20in (51cm); rooted hair; high-heeled walker; painted fingernails and toenails; jointed at neck, shoulders, hips, knees; various costumes; 1958.

SEE: *Illustration 131. Toys and Novelties*, March 1958.
PRICE: $20-45 (depending on costume)

Illustration 130.

Illustration 131.

Dolly Darling

The registered trademarks, the trademarks and the copyrights appearing in italics within this chapter belong to Dolly Darling.

Dolly Darling Patterns: "Make Beautiful Outfits for *Barbie®*, *Debbie®*, All Teen Dolls. Each great package includes Complete Patterns. Lovely Fabrics. Trimmings."

SEE: *Illustration 132. Workbasket*, November 1962. *Inga Tomletz Collection.*

Barbie® is a registered trademark of Mattel, Inc.
Debbie® is a registered trademark of Debbie Toy Company.

Illustration 132.

Eegee Goldberger Doll Mfg. Co., Inc.

The registered trademarks, the trademarks and the copyrights appearing in italics within this chapter belong to Eegee Goldberger Mfg. Co., Inc., unless otherwise noted.

This well-known company founded in 1917 continued their policy of making "look-alikes" from 1957 to 1965. These types included *Tammy®*, *Barbie®*, 10in (25cm) fashion high-heeled dolls and large "playpal-type" dolls. While many of their dolls were for the inexpensive mass market, they had well-designed dolls and clothing. Mollye Goldman was reputed to have worked for them and some of the costumes are exquisite.

Their line was varied and extensive; they also made wonderful specialties such as the *My Fair Lady Doll*.

Tammy® is a registered trademark of the Ideal Toy Corp.

Barbie® is a registered trademark of the Mattel, Inc.

Luv-able Skin Doll: Stuffed vinyl one-piece body; 18in (46cm); blonde rooted hair; exceptionally beautiful skin tone; sleep eyes with real lashes; blue eye shadow above eyes; painted eyelashes on corners and underneath eyes; earrings; individual fingers; bendable, poseable body and limbs; red velvet coat and hat with white trim; checked taffeta dress; nylon stockings; high-heel shoes; all original; circa 1957-58. Clothes reputed to be designed by Mollye Goldman.

    MARKS: "H//EEGEE" (head); "EEGEE//H18" (body); "Eegee's Luv-able Skin Doll; entirely of soft unbreakable vinyl//washable and unbreakable, will not peel, crack or chip//magic bend action-bends-kneels-sits."

    SEE: *Illustration 133* (doll).

           Illustration 134 (close-up of face).

    PRICE: $70-75 (mint condition only)

Illustration 133.   *Illustration 134.*

My Fair Lady: Rigid vinyl body; medium soft vinyl legs and arms; soft vinyl head; 19in (48cm); jointed at neck, shoulders, hips, waist; flat 14R face with beautiful skin tone; sleep eyes; feathered eyebrows; unusual eyelashes ʃʃʅʅ below eyes; closed-mouth; individual fingers with 3rd and 4th fingers curled; red fingernail polish; unusual brunette rooted hair with "thread-like" quality; high heeled; white lace dress with black velvet band at top of dress and around the hips similar to one from the movie by the same name; 1957.

> **MARKS:** "14R-1"(back of neck)
> **SEE:** *Illustration 135* (doll).
> *Peggy Murray Collection.*
> > *Illustration 136* (see advertisement *Toys and Novelties*, March 1957).
>
> **PRICE:** $85-90

Illustration 136.

Little Miss Debutante: Vinyl body and head; 10in (25cm); jointed at neck, shoulders, waist, hips; sleep eyes; very arched eyebrows; unusual face; wears earrings; high heeled; clothes all original; red and white striped dress with white lace and black ribbon trim; blonde rooted hair; 1958.

> Very similar to *Revlon*® doll.
> **MARKS:** "Eegee" (head); "Eegee's Little Debutante, all vinyl body, jointed waist"(purse tag)
> **SEE:** *Illustration 137.*
> **PRICE:** $30-40 (mint condition)

Revlon® is a registered trademark of Revlon, Inc.

Illustration 135.

Shelley: Stuffed vinyl; 8in (20cm) poseable doll that sits, kneels, sleeps; washable; rooted hair; has many changes of costumes.

> **MARKS:** "Eegee" (head)
> **SEE:** *Illustration 136* (bottom, *Toys and Novelties*, March 1957).
> **PRICE:** $20-30

Illustration 137.

Illustration 138.

Illustration 139.

Grow-hair Doll: All-plastic body with soft vinyl painted face; 12in (31cm); rooted blonde hair which grows when ring in back is pulled; open-mouth; four lashes at corners of eyes; 2nd, 3rd and 4th fingers molded together; *Tammy*® look-alike; 1964.

MARKS: "Eegee" (head)
SEE: *Illustration 140. Inga Tomoletz Collection.*
PRICE: $20

Illustration 141.

Barbie® Look-alike: Plastic body and legs; soft vinyl arms and head; 11½in (29cm); ponytail with bangs; 3rd and 4th fingers molded together; white iris eyes; light pink lips; clothes not original; circa 1961-63.

Some were called *Babette* and came boxed and dressed in a striped bathing suit.

MARKS: "E G" (head); or no mark
SEE: *Illustration 138* (close-up of face). *Marianne Gardner Collection.*

Illustration 139 (bodies). *Marianne Gardner Collection.*

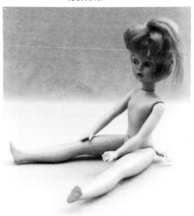

Illustration 140.

Puppetrina: Vinyl; 22½in (57cm); play action for little girls four to ten years old; their fingers make her act and do all the things they want her to do; dressed in sailor outfit with pleated skirt; additional wardrobe sets were available for sale.

SEE: *Illustration 141. Playthings,* August 1963.
PRICE: $45-65

Barbie® is a registered trademark of Mattel, Inc.

Tammy® is a registered trademark of the Ideal Toy Corp.

Girl in Pink Dress: Stuffed vinyl; 28in (71cm); sleep eyes; medium high heels; rooted curly hair; painted fingernails; lovely pink formal dress with pink net overskirt and slip; costume factory made and may be original; circa 1957-58.

This type of stuffed vinyl doll was similar to *Betty the Beautiful Bride®* by Deluxe Reading. Eegee dressed some of their high-heeled dolls in elegant clothes; they were often sold in such stores as Woolworth's, Kresge's, and so forth.

MARKS: "251//AE//Y29" (head); "103" (body)
SEE: *Illustration 142,* **see page 245.** *Schroeder Collection.*
PRICE: $35-45

Illustration 143.

Susan Stroller: Poly and vinyl; 32in (81cm); rooted pixie-cut hair; sleep eyes; dressed in blue nylon dress with embroidered band trim; attached slip; panties; 1961.

Also came in 20in (51cm); 23in (58cm); 26in (66cm) sizes.
SEE: *Illustration 143, Playthings,* March 1961.
PRICE: $85-100 (for 32in [81cm] size)

DOLLS NOT PHOTOGRAPHED

Tandy Talks: Plastic body and legs; vinyl arms and head; 21in (53cm); rooted blonde hair; open/closed mouth with four teeth; freckles; pull string talker that says four phrases; circa 1961.
MARKS: "15 P Eegee" (head)
PRICE: $50-60

Gemettes: Vinyl; 15½in (39cm); rooted hair; sleep eyes; jointed at neck, shoulders, hips; dresses reflected color of gems; child's simulated jewel ring was included; circa 1963.

Miss Emerald; Miss Amythyst; Miss Ruby; Miss Sapphire; Miss Diamond; Miss Topaz.
PRICE: $20-25 (all original)

Andy: Plastic body and legs; vinyl arms and head; 12in (31cm); *Ken®* look-alike; molded blonde hair; painted side-glancing eyes; jointed at neck, shoulders, hips; came in bathing trunks; circa 1961-1963.
MARKS: "E G-1961" (head and back)

Annette: Vinyl; 11½in (29cm) *Barbie®* look-alike; rooted hair; came in striped bathing suit like *Barbie®*, had a wardrobe which could be purchased separately; circa 1961-1963.
PRICE: $20-25 *Andy*
$20-25 *Annette*

Little Debutante: Vinyl with soft vinyl head; many sizes of high-heeled dolls; rooted hair; sleep eyes; closed-mouth; jointed at neck, shoulders, waist, hips; painted nails; teenage figure; many different costumes; head turning walker; rather "flat" face; circa 1957.

The name "Debutante" was used extensively by Eegee. The costumes were pretty and well done. Usually the name "Eegee" was incorporated in the marks on the doll.

Effanbee Doll Corporation

The registered trademarks, the trademarks and the copyrights appearing in italics within this chapter belong to Effanbee Doll Corporation.

Although Effanbee had a full line of dolls during the 1957-65 period, they did not always follow the same trends as other manufacturers. They did have a wonderful line of "grown-up" fashion dolls in the late 1950s with their *Honey Walker* and *Jr. Miss* lines, but in the early 1960s they emphasized the child dolls such as *Fluffy* and *Susie Sunshine*. They also made an unusual boy doll, *Mickey*, with many types of outfits. This doll sold well and was so dearly loved that it is rare to find him in an unplayed-with condition.

They did follow the general trend of making large dolls, and their flirty-eyed *Mary Jane* was successful. They also revived their best seller of the 1930s, *Patsy*, in a vinyl version. She had a wardrobe which could be purchased separately.

Little Lady: Rigid vinyl body and soft vinyl head; 15in (38cm); sleep eyes; feathered eyebrows; 3rd and 4th fingers molded together; rooted hair; not in original clothes; 1954.

This is a very early vinyl doll which reused an old Effanbee name. She was in a box with "Little Lady Toiletries" designed by Helene Pessl, Incorporated. The dark haired doll on the left still has traces of her tight "sausage" curls.

MARKS: "Effanbee" (head and back)

SEE: *Illustration 144. Barbara Comienski Collection.*

PRICE: Not enough samples of doll in original box with toiletries to price.

$30-50 (in good condition; not in original clothes)

Illustration 144.

Mickey:

Mickey was introduced in 1956. He was 10in (25cm), and he came as a football player, fireman, soldier, sailor, policeman and baseball player.

By 1959 *Mickey* had grown to 10½in (27cm), and he also came as a jockey,

Boy Scout, bellhop, air cadet, hunter, marine, boxer with robe, boxer without robe, cowboy, Cub Scout, clown and a sports figure with a cloth hat.

By 1960 *Mickey* was 11in (28cm) and had added *Johnny Reb* and *Yankee Boy*. The difference in height can be clearly seen in the illustration.

The two dolls on the left are 11in (28cm). The football player is 10½in (27cm) and the little baseball player is 10in (25cm).

There are differences in the markings of the *Mickey* dolls.

Mickey dolls in good condition are rare. They were so greatly beloved and played with that often their hats were well-chewed.

From left to right:

Mickey Baseball Player: Soft vinyl; 11in (28cm); painted eyes with freckles above nose; molded hair and hat; "watermelon-type" mouth; individual fingers; white flannel baseball uniform with red stripes and hat; #5 on back; all original; 1960-63.

MARKS: "Effanbee" (head); "10//Effanbee//8" (back)

Mickey Sailor: Soft vinyl; 11in (28cm); dark blue naval sailor uniform with molded-on white sailor hat; middy collar with white trim; sailor tie; circa 1960-1963.

MARKS: "Mickey//Effanbee" (head); "©//F-B" (back)

The authors own another sailor which is 10½in (27cm). It is marked "Mickey//Effanbee" on head; "10 Effanbee//8" on back of body.

Mickey Football Player: Soft vinyl; 10½in (25cm); football uniform has white flannel top with red stripes down arms; red twill pants with white stripe down the side of the pants; originally it had a "45" on the front of the shirt; circa 1959.

MARKS: "Effanbee" (head); no marks on back of body

Mickey Baseball Player: All vinyl; 10in (25cm); white flannel baseball uniform with blue stripes; blue molded baseball cap; holds bat; circa 1956.

MARKS: "Effanbee" (head); no marks on back of body
SEE: *Illustration 145.*
PRICE: $80-100 (mint condition)
　　　　$25-50 (played with condition)

Illustration 145.

Honey Walker: These two dolls are very unusual. They were in their boxes and came from the same collection. Both are exactly alike except for the feet. The doll on the left has very high-heeled feet and is 21in (53cm) tall. The doll on the right has jointed ankles and medium heels and is 20in (51cm) tall. All other characteristics are the same.

Hard plastic body and legs; soft vinyl head; medium soft vinyl arms; rooted hair; sleep eyes with real lashes; painted eyelashes to side and underneath eyes; high arched eyebrows; pierced ears with pearl teardrop earrings; jointed at neck, shoulder, hips, just above the knees; smaller one is jointed at the ankles; head turning walking mechanism; individual fingers with a diamond-type ring on the 4th finger of the left hand; 1957-1958.

Doll on left: red taffeta dress with lace trim; beige straw hat with red net and flowers; black high-heeled shoes; necklace of pearls.

Doll on right: heavy embossed brown, white and black print glazed cotton dress; high neckline; red medium-heeled shoes; pearl necklace and earrings.

MARKS: "Effanbee" (head); "I am *Honey Walker*" (tag)

SEE: *Illustration 146.*

PRICE: $125-150 (each doll)

Jr. Miss Bride: Rigisol vinyl plastic body, legs, arms, head; 19in (48cm); jointed at neck, shoulders, waist, hips; high-heel feet; blonde rooted hair; sleep eyes with real lashes; closed-mouth; individual fingers with 3rd and 4th fingers curled inward; painted fingernails and toenails; dressed in long white satin dress with three-tier overskirt trimmed with Venetian lace; ruffled slip; panties; nylon stockings; high-heeled shoes; nylon gloves; ring, necklace and earrings; headpiece trimmed with flowers and long net veil; pictured in 1958 Effanbee catalog.

MARKS: "EFFANBEE" (head)

SEE: *Illustration 147.*

PRICE: $60-80

Illustration 146.

Illustration 147.

Illustration 148. Illustration 149.

Mary Jane: Plastic body with vinyl head; 32in (81cm); walking mechanism; freckles; flirty sleep eyes; 1959.
Fashions include:
1. Red organdy dress with white apron.
2. Nurse's uniform.
3. Striped dress with puffed sleeves.
   SEE: *Illustration 148. Playthings*, March 1959.
   PRICE: $120-150

Girl Scout and Campfire Girls Dolls:
For many years Effanbee made official Brownie, Girl Scout, Bluebird and Campfire dolls. They used different molds for these dolls from 1957 to 1965.
1. *Fluffy*, circa 1957-65, 11in (28cm).
2. *Patsy Ann*, circa 1960, 15in (38cm).
3. *Suzette*, circa 1962, 15in (38cm).
4. All-vinyl, circa 1964, 16in (41cm) doll.
4. *Official Junior Girl Scout*, circa 1965, 8½in (21cm).

Fluffy Official Compfire Bluebird Doll: Head and body good quality soft vinyl; 11in (28cm); sleep eyes with molded lashes; painted lashes under eye; individual fingers; closed-mouth; two lines under knees; official Campfire uniform; dark blue skirt with red felt weskit and white blouse; felt tam with Campfire emblem; smiling face; good quality blonde rooted hair; circa 1957-1960.
MARKS: "FLUFFY//EFFANBEE" (head); "10//EFFANBEE//8" (body)
SEE: *Illustration 149* (doll on left).
PRICE: $50-65

Official Girl Scout #11-956: Head and body good quality soft vinyl; 8½in (22cm); rosy cheeks on black skin tone; excellent rooted hair; sleep eyes with molded lashes; painted lashes under eyes; 3rd and 4th fingers molded together; two dimples on each knee; official green uniform of Girl Scouts and felt tam with Girl Scout emblem; 1965.
MARKS: "EFFANBEE ©1965" (head); "Girl GS Scouts//Official Junior Girl Scout//11-956" (box)
SEE: *Illustration 149* (doll on right).
PRICE: $40-45

Patsy Ann: Rigisol vinyl with soft vinyl head; 15in (38cm); rooted Saran hair that could be washed and set; freckles around nose; jointed at neck, shoulders, hips; dressed in official Girl Scout uniform; 1959-1961.

Patsy Ann had many different outfits including a calico print dress; embroidered cotton dress; checked gingham dress, ballerina costume; skating costume; majorette outfit; official Brownie uniform; doll and wardrobe packages.

MARKS: "Effanbee//Patsy Ann//©1959" (head); "E F F A N B E E" (back)
SEE: *Illustration 150. Ann N. Condron Collection.*
PRICE: $90-100

Illustration 150.

Illustration 151.

Suzie Sunshine: All vinyl; 18in (46cm); jointed at neck, shoulders, hips; rooted hair; sleep eyes with lashes; freckles around the nose; designed by Eugenia Dukas; circa 1961-1981.

This particular doll was very popular and was kept in the line for many years. She came in a wide variety of outfits and in the later years was regularly used in different series. In 1963 the Sears catalog had *Suzie* as a *Schoolgirl Writing Doll* with a molded hand to hold the crayon.

SEE: *Illustration 151. Inga Tomoletz Collection.*
PRICE: Various prices depending on year of production and costume.

Illustration 152.

Belle-Telle and Her Talking Telephone: Plastic with soft vinyl head; 18in (46cm); advertisement says, "Belle-Telle and her realistic talking telephone will capture the heart of every little girl. She holds the receiver to her ear so naturally. Her hand is sculptured to hold almost anything. Her telephone is so simple to operate...just push the magic button and the conversation will start. And it says ever so many things. (Operates on Flashlight Battery)." She says 11 phrases by using a concealed record; 1962.

SEE: *Illustration 152. Playthings*, September 1962.
PRICE: $75-95 (in operating condition)

Miss Chips Bride: Plastic legs and body; soft vinyl arms and head; 17in (43cm) blonde rooted hair; sleep eyes with real lashes; three painted lashes at side of each eye; rosy cheeks; closed-mouth; jointed at neck, shoulders, legs; individual fingers with 3rd and 4th fingers curled inward; lace and tulle bridal gown over taffeta slip; panties, crinoline, stockings; satin shoes; lace-trimmed bridal veil with flowers on crown; single blue garter; doll marked "1965," but this bridal costume was in the 1968 Effanbee catalog.

MARKS: "Effanbee//19©65// 1700"

SEE: *Illustration 153.*

PRICE: $65-75

Illustration 153.

DOLLS NOT PHOTOGRAPHED

Alyssa: Rigisol vinyl; 24in (61cm); jointed at neck, shoulders, hips, elbow; rooted Saran hair; sleep eyes; flat feet; came dressed as a bride or bridesmaid; also came with street clothes or party dress; circa 1960.

Bud: Rigisol vinyl; 24in (61cm); jointed at neck, shoulders, hips, elbows; molded hair; sleep eyes; dressed in gingham checked shirt with corduroy pants; shoes and socks; circa 1960.

Happy Boy: Vinyl; 11in (28cm); character face with "watermelon-type" mouth; molded hair; three dolls in series:
1. in checked shirt and jeans
2. in nightgown and cap
3. in boxing trunks and gloves; circa 1960

Little Lady: Vinyl; 20in (51cm); sleep eyes; rooted hair; jointed at neck, hips, shoulders; came as bride; circa 1959.

Little Lady: Vinyl; 19in (48cm); jointed at neck, shoulders, hips; sleep eyes; rooted hair; pigtails; checked gingham dress; flat feet; 1958 catalog.

Alice: Vinyl; 15in (38cm) and 19in (48cm); rooted Saran hair; dressed in organdy dress with organdy pinafore; held mirror; flat feet; circa 1958.

Suzette: Vinyl; 15in (38cm); jointed at neck, shoulders, hips; rooted hair; sleep eyes; dressed in checked school dress; plaid school dress; taffeta party dress; bridal gown of nylon lace and net; Blue Bird uniform; Campfire Girl uniform; Brownie uniform; Girl Scout uniform; circa 1959-1962. Other outfits include striped cotton dress; broadcloth dress; gingham slacks and matching top; sailor dress.

Boudoir Doll: Nylon cloth body; vinyl arms and legs; 28in (71cm); rooted hair; sleep eyes; long legs; circa 1959-61.

Schoolgirl Writing Doll: Suzie Sunshine mold used; vinyl; 18in (46cm); unusual molded hand held crayon; arm was ball-jointed for movement; circa 1963.

Electrosolids Corporation (ELSCO)

The registered trademarks, the trademarks and the copyrights appearing in italics within this chapter belong to Electrosolids Corporation.

Ellie Echo, the Famous Tape Recorder Doll: 24in (61cm); blonde cap cut hairdo; doll on left has pink checked party pinafore dress; green satin hair ribbon; panties; white socks; Peter Pan shoes; doll on right has blonde ponytail hairdo; pink checked play dress; pink ribbon; panties; white socks; Peter Pan shoes; has an endless 20-second tape transistorized and run by ordinary flashlight batteries.

"To operate *Ellie*, slide the middle button on her back to the right to record. Slide it to the left to listen. Center position is off. Talk directly to her when recording. She repeats what you say clearly and distinctly."

MARKS: Packaged in a telephone booth display carton which says, *"Ellie Echo"*
SEE: *Illustration 153A. Playthings,* September 1962, **see page 244.**
PRICE: Not enough samples available.

Elite Creations Inc.

The registered trademarks, the trademarks and the copyrights appearing in italics within this chapter belong to Elite Creations Inc., unless otherwise noted.

Illustration 153B.

Bonnie: Plastic; 11½in (29cm); *Barbie®* look-alike with ponytail and bangs; jointed at neck, shoulders, hips; high heels with shoes; elongated neck, black and white striped bathing suit; four fingers molded together; 1962.
    SEE: *Illustration 153B. Playthings*, March 1962.
    PRICE: $20-25

Wendy: Plastic; 11½in (29cm); *Barbie®* look-alike with swirl ponytail; jointed at neck, shoulders, hips; high heeled; elongated neck, red bathing suit; four fingers molded together; circa 1963-64.
    Wendy Wardrobe: Cotton dress in box with pink, red and white shirt with white blouse trimmed in red; extra pair of shoes; circa 1962-1963.
    The back of the dress box says, "This wardrobe is one of the many beautiful outfits to fit all 11½in (29cm) 'high fashion dolls.' "

    MARKS: None on doll; "Wendy" (box); "#38 Made in Hong Kong" (bathing suit)
    SEE: *Illustration 153C,* **page 244.**
    PRICE: $20-25

Barbie® is a registered trademark of Mattel, Inc.

Eugene Dolls

The registered trademarks, the trademarks and the copyrights appearing in italics within this chapter belong to Eugene Dolls.

My Little Lady: Vinyl; soft vinyl head; 18in (46cm) and 20in (51cm); rooted hair; sleep eyes; jacket, hat, bag made of fur; taffeta dress; nylon hose; high-heeled feet and shoes; 1957.

Illustration 154.

> **SEE:** *Illustration 154. Toys and Novelties,* July 1957.
> **PRICE:** $35-45 (18in [46cm] with fur jacket)
> $45-55 (20in [51cm] with fur jacket)

14R Dolls

This is not a company but a mark used on many dolls during the years from 1957 to 1965. These dolls were not all made the same and it is difficult to attribute them to one company.

There are a few characteristics which they have in common:

1. They have a "flat" face which is readily recognizable.
2. For the most part they were high-heeled, high fashion dolls with mature clothes. Most of the dolls seem to be 19in (48cm) or 20in (51cm).
3. The clothes were "flashy" and appealing. Often the costumes included such things as real and mock fur, flamboyant evening gowns, beautiful hats and nylon stockings.
4. They were usually the less expensive dolls made for marketing companies. Sometimes they were dressed by these companies but other times sales companies purchased them for resale fully-dressed.

The differences in these dolls include:

1. Their body parts are made of different types of materials such as hard plastic, soft vinyl, rigid vinyl, plastic and stuffed vinyl, depending on the year of manufacture and the final selling price.
2. The painting and finishing of the face varies among these dolls. Some of the dolls have excellent workmanship. Others were put together quickly on a mass assembly line.
3. The material and sewing of the clothing varies in quality.
4. The design of the clothing ranges from excellent to poor depending on the designer. Mollye Goldman is reputed to have designed beautiful clothes for one or more of these companies.

The following companies are known to have used dolls marked with 14R alone or in combination with other numbers or letters.

1. Belle
2. Deluxe Reading or one of their marketing companies
3. Eegee (See *Illustration 135.*)
4. Natural
5. Rite Lee
6. Royal
7. Sayco (See *Illustration 379.*)
   PRICE: Varies greatly

Girl in Black Fur Coat: Rigid vinyl body; soft vinyl head; 20in (51cm); sleep eyes; rooted blonde hair; painted eyelashes under eyes; beautiful skin color; toenails painted red; high heeled; Persian lamb coat and hat; white gloves; white net scarf; black shoes; stockings; purple rayon dress; circa 1957-1959. This doll is an example of a high quality 14R doll. The clothes are well designed and made. It was won at a carnival.
   MARKS: "14R" (head)
   SEE: *Illustration 155. Donald R. Kallar Collection.*
   PRICE: $35-45

Girl: Rigid vinyl body and limbs; soft vinyl head; 19in (48cm) brunette rooted hair; sleep eyes with lashes; painted lashes under eyes; pearl earrings; individual fingers; large breasts; jointed at neck, shoulders, waist, hips; all original red nylon dress with attached red taffeta slip; dark blue trim; white mock fur "chubby" coat; high-heeled feet; circa 1957-59.
   MARKS: "14R" (head)
   SEE: *Illustration 156.*
   PRICE: $20-25

Illustration 155.   *Illustration 156.*   *Illustration 157.*

Teenage Girl: Rigid vinyl body and legs; soft vinyl head and arms; 20in (51cm); sleep green eyes; three lines painted at corners of eyes; painted fingernails and toenails; earrings; clothes not original; circa 1957-1959.
   MARKS: "AE 2006//14R" (head)
   SEE: *Illustration 157. Jacki O'Connor Collection.*
   PRICE: $15-20

Fab-Lu Limited

The registered trademarks, the trademarks and the copyrights appearing in italics within this chapter belong to Fab-Lu Limited, unless otherwise noted.

This company made a *Barbie®* and *Ken®* look-alike dolls called *Babs* and *Bill*. The wardrobes imitated the Mattel clothing.

Randy, Bab's sister, was an Ideal *Tammy®* look-alike, and she, too, had a wardrobe similar to *Tammy®*.

Fab-Lu was known to have used dolls made in Hong Kong. *Babs* may be one of the dolls collectors now call "Hong Kong Lilli" or "Hong Kong Barbie."

The Fab-Lu company claimed that the doll clothes were "exacting copies of couturier fashions." In spite of the low cost of the boxed outfits ($1.00-1.49), the outfits were exciting to children and faithful to the fashions of the early 1960s. For the period, these clothes were avant garde and "daring."

Because these dolls and clothes were "play" dolls for children, it is difficult to find them complete with all their accessories. However, the brochure is a miniature history of a glamorous fashion period for both adults and dolls.

Fab-Lu brochure showing the wardrobes of *Babs, Randy, Bill*.

Top row from left to right:
1. Examples of the 66 complete outfits in their boxes.
2. Cover showing *Randy*.

Bottom row from left to right:
1. *Let's Dance//Haute Mode*: formal short dress with one shoulder bare; high-heeled shoes; corsage which doubles as head piece.
2. *Queen of Hearts*: backless, strapless, striped cotton dress; purse; floral bouquet; goggles; beach sandals.
3. *Bill's Beachcomber*: terry cloth robe with matching slippers; man-sized Turkish towel; to be worn over *Bill's* bathing trunks.
4. *Bill's 50 Mile Hike*: Pullover sweater; gabardine slacks; cap; socks; hiking shoes.
   SEE: *Illustration 158.*
   PRICE: $35-50 (*Babs* mint-in-box)
   $25-40 (*Bill* mint-in-box)
   $10 (outfits mint-in-box)

| *Illustration 158.* | *Illustration 159.* | *Illustration 160.* |

Fab-Lu brochure

Top row left to right:

1. Note to Mothers: "Your choice of 66 complete ensembles fashion-inspired by World-Famous Couturiers in Paris, Rome and New York." The note reminded mothers that just as they teach good grooming to their daughters, they should help them acquire a fashion flair.
2. Pictures of *Randy, Bill, Babs* in the box with *Randy* standing in front.

Bottom row left to right:

1. *Bill* in a tuxedo.
2. Introducing *Babs*: Sturdy plastic in living flesh tones; 11½in (29cm); jointed at neck, shoulders, hips; hair in blonde, red, brunette, black; special plastic platform helps her keep her balance. The basic doll came with a striped swim suit; beach clogs; sunglasses; Scotty dog; purse with panties in it.
   MARKS: Possible ⬚F⬚ (hip)
   SEE: *Illustration 159.*

Fab-Lu brochure

Top row left to right:

1. *Beach Beauty*: three-piece playsuit; purse; beach shoes; goggles.
2. *Summer Delight*: strapless jersey sheath; matching sweater with braid binding; dancing shoes; vanity; harlequin glasses; orchid corsage.
3. *Bill's 19th Hole*: two-toned pullover; creased slacks; shoes; socks.
4. *Bill's Beau Brummel*: plaid suit with cuffed trousers; white shirt; red bow tie; socks; brown brogans.

Bottom row left to right:

1. *Light of Love*: satin-lined silver sheath dress with shimmering roses; dancing slippers; orchids.
2. *Date Bait*: one-piece frock with flared skirt and sleeveless bodice; purse; high fashion footwear; dog.
3. Introducing *Bill*: plastic; 11½in (29cm); molded, painted crew cut; jointed neck, shoulders, hips; long legs; powerful physique; balanced so he stands without a platform.
   SEE: *Illustration 160.*

Fab-Lu brochure

Top row left to right:

1. *Bill's Quiet Evening*: jacquard belted robe; matching slippers.
2. *Bill's Sports Afield*: knee-length shorts; polo shirt; sports shoes; socks.
3. *Golden Charmer*: strapless gold brocade sheath with ruffle at hemline; evening slippers; orchid corsage.
4. *Walking the Dog*: velveteen slacks with real zipper in front; open-toes sandals; sunglasses; puppy dog.

Bottom row from left to right:

1. *Bill's Sports Ensemble*: lined sports jacket; tailored slacks; sports shirt; socks; loafers.
2. *Bill's Sleep Walker*: figure-striped pajamas with manufacturer's label; matching slippers.
3. *Let's Go Formal!*: satin skirt with lace overskirt; gold brocade bodice; tulle covers bare shoulders; dance pumps; orchid corsage.

4. *Slim Silhouette*: sleeveless floral print dress with cowl neckline; high-fashion shoes; floral bouquet.

    SEE: *Illustration 161.*

Illustration 161.   *Illustration 162.*

Fab-Lu brochure

Top row left to right:

1. *Cummerbund Cutie*: gingham dress flecked with gold thread; long sleeves; open-toed shoes; floral bouquet.
2. *Ain't She Cute*: knitted jersey slack suit with turtle neck; shoes; dog.
3. *Randy's Let It Rain!*: velvet-collared storm coat; matching kerchief; low-heeled slippers; purse.
4. *Randy's Bull's Eye*: hooded T-shirt; denim pants; white shoes; bow and three quivers; target with tripod.

Bottom row left to right:

1. *Sugar 'n Spice*: strapless, backless sundress in candy stripes; sandals, floral accessories; sunglasses.
2. *Bon Voyage!*: velveteen suit dress; fur-trimmed coat; shoes; purse.
3. *Randy's Clam Digger*: striped jersey T-shirt; clam digger pants; matching hair ribbon; picnic hamper; tablecloth; sun goggles; beach shoes; transistor radio.
4. *Randy's Home Alone*: tailored slacks; lace-trimmed satin over blouse; high-fashioned footwear; telephone; glasses.

    SEE: *Illustration 162.*

Illustration 163.

Illustration 164.

Fab-Lu brochure

Top row left to right:

1. *Randy's Hip Hip Hooray!:* cheerleader with turtlenecked sweater; ballerina skirt; ruffled panties; cheerleader's cap and shoes; baton, megaphone.
2. *Randy's Bermuda Bound:* Bermuda shorts; tailored over blouse; beach shoes; purse; sun goggles.
3. *Rip Tide:* halter-top sunsuit; beach jacket; cover-up skirt; purse; goggles; beach clogs.
4. *Slack Suit:* gabardine tapered slacks; matching jacket with crest insignia; knit blouse; goggles; beach sandals.

Bottom row left to right:

1. *Randy's Beauty and the Beast:* peppermint cotton skirt and blouse; short shorts; purse; dog.
2. *Randy's Park Avenue:* lace-trimmed satin over blouse; velveteen slacks; evening sandals; telephone; transistor radio.
3. *Shopper Stopper:* short jersey coat with stand-up collar; cowl-necked shirtwaist; straight tweed skirt; purse; goggles; shoes.
4. *Floradora:* floral print dress; high neck; half sleeves; purse; pumps; floral corsage.
   SEE: *Illustration 163.*

Fab-Lu brochure

Top row left to right:

1. *Randy's Queen of the Courts:* white tennis dress; shirred panties; sneakers; tennis racket in press.
2. *Randy's Special Occasion:* brocade dress; silk-lined bolero; velvet bodice with gold shoulder straps; high-heeled dance slippers; orchid.
3. *Dream Girl:* sheath dress in a floral brocade hand print; dance pumps; orchid.
4. *Puttin' on the Ritz:* haute mode brocade, full-skirted gold and silver dinner dress; dance pumps; orchids.

Bottom row left to right:

1. *Happy Wedding Day!:* twin-tiered embossed organdy gown over satin slip; sheer veil encircling band of shimmering pearls with delicate ruching.
2. *Arabesque:* at home costume with flared skirt; oriental brocade; gold-threaded rickrack; tapered velveteen pants; harlequin glasses.
3. *Blaze of Glory:* evening coat of hand-painted flowered satin; low neckline; flared skirt; purse; harlequin glasses.
   SEE: *Illustration 164.*

Fab-Lu brochure

Top row left to right:

1. *Femme Fatale:* strapless sheath of filmy organdy over glittering satin; flounce at hem of skirt; dancing shoes; corsage.
2. *Candlelight:* high-fashion sheath with lowered hemline; matching bolero; high-heeled shoes.
3. Introducing *Randy:* As you will note by her young teenage wardrobe, *Randy* is much less sophisticated than her sister. However, she, too, is extremely fashion conscious and her extensive wardrobe of 18 outfits has a special appeal to the younger set.

Bottom row left to right:

1. *Creme Puff:* candy-striped cotton dress; overskirt of sheer organdy; purse; pumps; dog.

2. *Fashion Whirl*: strapless tight fitting bodice; satin full skirt; floral headdress; high-heeled pumps.
3. *Fifth Avenue*: two-piece tailored suit; jacket lined with same material as blouse; printed blouse; peg-topped fashion skirt; purse; slippers.
4. *Evening in Paris*: opera coat of gold and silver brocade; deep cuffs.
   SEE: *Illustration 165.*

Fab-Lu brochure
Top row left to right:
1. *Pert & Pretty*: designer polka dot dress with front skirt panel of a different color; snap-open purse; sandals; dog.
2. *Bare Midriff*: sleeveless topper that ties in front; well-tailored short shorts; wide waist; goggles; beach clogs; purse; puppy dog.
3. *Randy's Flair for Fun*: checked blouse with collar and cuffs; unicolored flaired skirt; snap-open purse; slippers; sunglasses.
4. *Randy's Snow Fun*: ski pants; fur-trimmed parka; intricately made skis; ski poles; goggles; transistor radio.

Bottom row left to right:
1. *Peek-a-Boo*: long sleeved lace blouse; bouffant skirt; white satin bra; high-heeled shoes; floral corsage.
2. *Formal Reception*: one-piece sheath; matching jacket lined with satin; shoes; orchids.
3. *Randy's Jumping Jiminy!*: black velveteen jumper; petite-lace blouse; gold cinch belt; pink slippers; snap-open vanity; transistor radio.
4. *Randy's Tea for Two*: lined afternoon dress; bouffant organdy skirt appliqued with delicate embroidery; velvet sash; matching hair ribbon; snap-open vanity purse; slippers.
   SEE: *Illustration 166.*

Illustration 165.

Illustration 166.

Fab-Lu brochure
Top row left to right:
1. *Randy's Everybody's Sweetheart*: dress with unicolored top; flared skirt; short sleeved jacket lined with matching material; snap-open vanity purse; low-heeled pumps.
2. *Randy's Low Tide*: one-piece bathing suit with decollete front; fringe-trimmed poncho; beach clogs; sun goggles; transistor radio.
3. *Big Bertha*: Bertha collar on taffeta dress; dance pumps; snap-open purse.

4. *RSVP*: lace-over-satin sheath, backless and strapless; lace bolero; dancing shoes, orchid.

Illustration 167.

Illustration 168.

Bottom row left to right:

1. *Randy's Sleep Tight!*: lace sleep ensemble; full-length dressing gown; slippers; brush; comb and mirror set.
2. *Randy's Outdoor Girl*: red hunter's cap; flared gabardine jacket with wide leather belt with buckle; slacks; shoes; purse; sunglasses.
3. *Sun-back Sensation*: summer cotton dress; snap-open purse; goggles; open-toed shoes; Scottie dog.
4. *Pastel Parfait*: printed satin floral dress, strapless and backless; bouffant skirt; vanity purse; dancing shoes; corsage.
   SEE: *Illustration 167.*

Randy the Teen Age Girl Doll: Hollow plastic body and legs; vinyl arms and head; 11½in (29cm); blue sleep eyes with molded lashes; dark red rooted hair; closed pink mouth; jointed at neck, shoulders, legs; green top with white nylon sleeves and collar; black ribbed tights; black plastic shoes; clothes all original; long neck; 18 outfits could be purchased; circa 1964.

MARKS: None on doll; "Randy the Teenage Girl Doll" (bubble package)
SEE: *Illustration 168.*
PRICE: $15-20

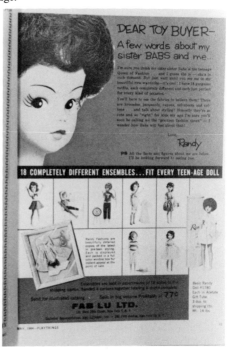

Illustration 169.

Randy: For general characteristics, see *Illustration 168;* advertised in *Playthings,* May 1964; 18 completely different ensembles including cheer leader costume, ski outfit, archery slacks and top; sleep ensemble, daytime dresses, pedal pushers and party dresses.
SEE: *Illustration 169.*

General Foods

The registered trademarks, the trademarks and the copyrights appearing in italics within this chapter belong to General Foods.

Linda Williams: Plastic body; 15in (38cm) rooted hair; sleep eyes; feathered eyebrows; painted eyelashes under eyes; jointed at neck, shoulders, hips; ⁇ on seat; vinyl face molded in portrait fashion; painted teeth; circa 1961.

Doll on left is small doll representing Angela Cartwright who played the character "Linda Williams" on the "Make Room for Daddy" television show.

Doll on right is the larger version of the television star (see *Illustration 326*). General Mills offered the smaller doll and a wardrobe as a premium. There was a brochure in the box which told about the extra clothes.

MARKS: "Linda Williams" (head)
SEE: *Illustration 170.*
PRICE: $40-50 (in original outfit only)

Gilbert, Manufactured By Ideal Toy Company, Marketed By Gilbert

The registered trademarks, the trademarks and the copyrights appearing in italics within this chapter belong to Gilbert, Ideal Toy Company.

James Bond 007: Plastic body, legs; vinyl head and arms; 12½in (32cm); molded hair; painted face; hand sculptured to hold gun and other accessories; white shirt; blue bathing suit; black flippers and mask; 1965.

MARKS: "Ideal Toy Co//B 12½-2" (doll); "James Bond/007 Action//Figure" (box)
SEE: *Illustration 171. Chuck and Carole Correll Collection.*
PRICE: $80-100

Illustration 170.

Illustration 171.

Gladtoy Toy Company, Brookglad Corp.

The registered trademarks, the trademarks and the copyrights appearing in italics within this chapter belong to Gladtoy Toy Company, Brookglad Corp.

Poor Pitiful Pearl: Stuffed vinyl body and head; 16in (41cm); jointed at neck only; sleep eyes with lashes; watermelon mouth; large ears; not original clothes; circa 1958-59.

These dolls were very pliable when they were first made. However, now they crack very easily. Early advertisements say, "She sits, kneels, bends." See also Horsman, page 121.

MARKS: "Gladtoy" (head)

SEE: *Illustration 172* (advertisement *Toys and Novelties*, March 1957).

Illustration 173 (doll).

PRICE: $20-50

Illustration 172.

Illustration 173.

Hasbro, Hasenfield Bros. Inc.

The registered trademarks, the trademarks and the copyrights appearing in italics within this chapter belong to Hasbro, Hasenfeld Bros Inc., unless otherwise noted.

Illustration 174.

G.I. Joe: He was introduced in 1964 and the advertisement in *Illustration 174* appeared in *Playthings*. He was a plastic doll measuring over 11in (28cm) with molded hair and painted features. Like *Barbie®*, he had his own world of clothes, uniforms and accessories. Also like *Barbie®*, he is still very popular.

This 1964 advertisement says "*G.I. Joe* is four different people...an action soldier, action sailor, action marine, action pilot...with 21 movable parts he sits, stands, and kneels...takes every possible military position...all scaled from authentic TIC government issue in the Army, Navy, Corps. and Air Force."

Today he is highly collectible and has many devoted fans. Like the *Barbie®* fans, this group of collectors has now matured and they are now expanding their collections and trying to find that elusive uniform or accessory that they missed in their childhood.

Much has been published about *G.I. Joe*, and it is not within the scope of this book to publish catalogs, brochures or prices. However, both then and now, *G.I. Joe* does take his place with other "wardrobe" dolls of this period.

SEE: *Illustration 174. Playthings*, June 1964.

Dotty Darlings: Vinyl; 4in (10cm); hat box dolls; six different dolls with miniature clothes and accessories.
1. *Karen Has a Slumber Party*; shorty pajamas; portable phonograph; record albums; cosmetics.
2. *Suzy Goes to School.*
3. *Beth at the Supermarket.*
4. *Kathy Goes to a Party.*
5. *John Has His Pets.*
6. *Shary Takes a Vacation.*
Dolls were advertised on television in almost 100 markets.
    MARKS: Unknown
    SEE: *Illustration 175. Playthir.*
    June 1965.
    PRICE: $12-15 (in case)
Barbie® is a registered trademark of Mattel, Inc.

Illustration 175.

Hollywood Doll Manufacturing Company

Little One: Flexible vinyl; 7in (18cm); high-heeled in own picture frame; 24 "Make Believe outfits"; a "Joanie Kay Original."
The costumes include:
"I visit a country garden and make believe I am"
1. A Lily-of-the Valley
2. A Bluebell
3. A Buttercup
4. A Petunia.
"I visit the Land of Fairies...and make believe I am"
1. The Rainbow Fairy
2. The Sugar Plum Fairy
3. The Forest Fairy

Illustration 176.

4. The Orchid Fairy
"I visit the Land of Magic...and make believe I am"
1. The Princess of the Night
2. The Princess of the Moon
3. The Princess of the Rose
4. The Princess of the Sun
"I visit Storyland...and make believe I am"
1. Bo-Peep
2. Heidi
3. Miss Muffet
4. Gretel
5. Pollyanna
6. Alice
"As I change the color of my basic dress,
I make believe I change the color of my hair"

1. Dress blue - hair platinum
2. Dress rose - hair gold
3. Dress red - hair honey
4. Dress green - hair auburn
5. Dress yellow - hair brunette

6. Dress white - hair ebony.
The dolls could be purchased in just a lace-trimmed camisole slip or purchased in one of the costumes. Other costumes were sold separately.

Inez Holland created the fairy tale character, and she wrote a story which was published along with the advertisement in the April 1959 issue of *Toys and Novelties.*

PRICE: $20-30 (all original in picture frame box)
$8-10 for (doll alone)
SEE: *Illustration 176.*

Horsman Dolls, Inc.

E.I. Horsman, the founder of the Horsman company and a pioneer in the production of the modern indestructible doll, would have been proud of the variety of dolls his company produced from 1957 to 1965.

In 1957 the company created a Couturier's division for dolls in the "fashion spotlight." These dolls had beautiful fashions created by excellent costume designers. They used the Horsman name *Cindy* for many of the dolls in this line, but there were also other fashion dolls with different names and sizes.

In line with their emphasis on fashion dolls, Horsman created a *Jacqueline Kennedy* doll. The First Lady was a leader in the high fashion of the period.

The year 1965 was very special for this company. They celebrated their 100th birthday with Walt Disney's *Mary Poppins* and *Cinderella*. They also featured *Patty Duke*, Academy Award winner and star of her network television show. For Horsman it was a very good century.

Cindy: Rigid vinyl body with soft vinyl head; 19in (48cm); deep flesh tone for Horsman doll; red color on cheeks; blue glassine sleep eyes; painted eyelashes at side of each eye (eight on right and eight on left); earrings; rooted dark red curly hair; palms down facing body; swivel waist; legs have walking mechanism; head does not turn with walking mechanism; red painted fingernails and toenails; high-heeled feet: original pink nylon eyelet party dress with cowl neckline over pink rayon double slip; red and white nylon dress; fluffy blue cotton coat; circa 1957-59. Horsman used many variations of the nylon eyelet material.
    MARKS: "HORSMAN//83" (head)
    SEE: *Illustration 177* (doll and clothes).
    PRICE: $50-60

Illustration 177.

Illustration 178.

Cindy Bride: Rigid vinyl body and soft vinyl head; 19in (48.3cm); for general characteristics, see *Illustration 177;* dark red curly hair; painted eyelashes at sides of eyes; fingers and toes have no red polish; satin bride dress with satin inset at waist; satin bolero; satin slip; crinoline hoop; bouquet of cloth flowers; pearl necklace and earrings; stockings and high-heeled shoes; all original; circa 1957-59.

> **MARKS:** "HORSMAN 83" (head); "Another of//America's best-loved dolls// by//HORSMAN" (box)
> **SEE:** *Illustration 178.*

PRICE: $90-110

Cindy: In the February 1957 issue of *Toys and Novelties* they reported that Alan Cathcart, Managing Director, Plastics Division, Lines Brothers, Ltd., said, "American Dolls are too sophisticated for the children of the United Kingdom." He was speaking about the *Cindy* Horsman *Bride* shown in the picture.

> **SEE:** *Illustration 179. Toys and Novelties*, February 1957.

Illustration 179.

Illustration 180.

Cindy: Rigid vinyl body with soft vinyl head; 19in (48cm); blue glassine eyes; real eyelashes; rooted dark red curly hair; palms down facing body; unusual wooden ball-jointed elbows like *Renee Ballerina*; swivel waist; high-heeled feet; all original formal with black velvet top and rows of ruffled silver-shot nylon over a rayon slip; circa 1957-59.

> **MARKS:** "Horsman" (head)
> **SEE:** *Illustration 181. Ester Borgis Collection.*

PRICE: $50-60

Revlon® is a registered trademark of Revlon, Inc.

Cindy: Rigid vinyl body with soft vinyl head; 18in (46cm); competed with the *Revlon®* doll; rooted hair; sleep eyes with real eyelashes; slightly puckered closed-mouth; glassine sleep eyes; jointed at neck, shoulders, hips and just above the knees; pink nylon eyelet formal with black velvet sash; high heels; nylon stockings; all original; 1957.

> **MARKS:** "88//HORSMAN" (head); "B18 (or 818)//Pat. 2736135" (body)
> **SEE:** *Illustration 180. Patricia Dycus Callender Collection.*

PRICE: $50-60

Illustration 181.

Illustration 182.

Cindy: Rigid vinyl body, soft vinyl head; 10½in (27cm); blue sleep eyes with molded eyelashes; four painted slanted eyelashes on top side of each eye; red lips, finger and toenails; pierced ears; 3rd and 4th fingers molded together; long blonde rooted hair that could be washed and curled but the quality is not as good as other dolls such as *Miss Revlon®*, *Toni®* or *Ginger®*; "hat box" tag reads, "Horsman's Cindy//Negligee//All Vinyl Plastic//Washable; Rooted Hair// High Heels//Turning Body;" swivel waist; black net negligee trimmed with pink lace; bra and girdle; separate fashions available circa 1958.

> **MARKS:** "HORSMAN" on back of head.
> **SEE:** *Illustration 182.*
> **PRICE:** $60 (doll in original box)
> $45-55 (doll)

Couturier's Lady: Stuffed vinyl body and head; 19in (48cm); rooted platinum hair pulled on top of head in curls; for general characteristics, see *Illustration 185;* all original; form fitting simple black velvet dress with large flounce at hem of dress; white satin cowl-style collar with one large deep red rose; circa 1957-58.

> **MARKS:** "83//HORSMAN" (head)
> **SEE:** *Illustration 183.*
> **PRICE:** $40-50+ (all original in mint conditio
> $10-25 (original but poor vinyl)

Couturier Dolls: The advertisement from *Playthings*, February 1958, showed two dolls that were stuffed vinyl with unusual ball-jointed elbows. They had several unusual hair colors. The advertisement announced, "The first anniversary of the successful debut in the doll fashion spotlight."

These dolls were part of the "high fashion" dolls of the era. Stuffed vinyl dolls were a new concept that made these dolls very poseable and popular. Horsman, Eegee (see pages 118 and 92) and others often used famous designers for clothing. The stuffed

Revlon® is a registered trademark of Revlon, Inc.

Toni® is a registered trademark of The Gillette Co.

Ginger® is a registered trademark of the Cosmopolitan Toy and Doll Corporation.

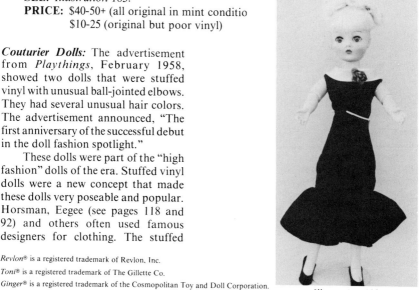

Illustration 183.

vinyl deteriorated rapidly when the child played with the doll and posed the arms and legs. Mint examples of this doll are beautiful and rare.

MARKS: "82 HORSMAN" and "83 HORSMAN"

SEE: *Illustration 184. Playthings,* February 1958.

PRICE: $40-50+ (all original in mint condition)

$10-25 (original but poor vinyl)

Illustration 184.

Illustration 185.

Tweedie: Advertisement from *Playthings,* February 1958; "See Tweedie at the Toy Fair and Everywhere. She appears on millions of packages of Tweedie Toiletries by Lentheric...sold, publicized, promoted from coast-to-coast."

Tweedie had a wonderful wardrobe from the famous designers and manufacturers of the day. These included *Bambury Coats, Love Dresses, Geisha Robes* and *Lounging Clothes, Regal Swimwear* and *Mr. John Juniorette Hats.*

MARKS: "38//HORSMAN" (head)

SEE: *Illustration 186. Playthings,* February 1958.

PRICE: $15-75 (depending on outfit)

Couturier's Renee Ballerina: Poseable stuffed soft vinyl body and head; 19in (48cm); rooted pink hair; beautiful skin color; sparkling glassine eyes; real eyelashes; closed-mouth; jointed at neck, arms, elbows; unusual ball-jointed elbows; individual fingers; V back side; long neck; high-heel feet; original white ballerina costume with net skirt and collar; satin top; long nylon stockings; pink vinyl ballerina shoes; white flowers at neck and collar; circa 1957-58.

This doll is not as rare or hard-to-find as some of the other *Couturier* dolls.

MARKS: "82//HORSMAN" (head). Some dolls came in box marked "Horsman Cindy."

SEE: *Illustration 185.*

PRICE: $25-30 (all original in mint condition)

$10-20 (original but poor vinyl)

Illustration 186.

Illustration 187.

Tweedie: Rigid vinyl body and soft vinyl head; 14½in (37cm); flat feet; glassine eyes; closed-mouth; purplish eyebrows characteristic of Horsman; sleep eyes; lashes painted below eyes; Ỿ on back side; white and black checked dress with red bow at neck; white collar and trim on sleeves; 1958. This doll dressed in designer clothes is difficult to find.

MARKS: "38//HORSMAN" (head)
SEE: *Illustration 187. Patricia Dycus Callender Collection.*
PRICE: $15-25 (doll in illustration)

Jackie: Rigid vinyl body and soft vinyl head; 25in (64cm); rooted black hair; blue sleep eyes with long lashes; closed-mouth; pronounced dark oval eyebrows; small waist; pierced ears; white Schiffli embroidered dress with cotton batiste shawl; bracelet with pearl hearts; 1961.

MARKS: "HORSMAN//19©61//JK 25//4" (head)
SEE: *Illustration 188* (doll). *Sandra Strater Collection.*
Illustration 189 (close-up of face). *Sandra Strater Collection.*
PRICE: $90-110

Illustration 188.

Illustration 189.

Poor Pitiful Pearl: Stuffed vinyl body and head; 16in (41cm); jointed at neck only; sleep eyes with lashes above eyes; watermelon mouth; large ears; original clothes; original brochure; 1963.

From the famous cartoon character created by award-winning cartoonist Wm. Steig.

MARKS: "©1963//Wm. Steig//Horsman" (head)
SEE: *Illustration 190. Maureen Edick Collection.*
PRICE: $65-85 (with brochure)

Illustration 190.

Illustration 191.

100th Birthday Celebration: An advertisement in *Playthings*, March 1965, proclaimed the 100th Birthday of the Horsman company. They featured Walt Disney's *Mary Poppins* and *Cinderella*. They also produced a *Patty Duke* doll.
SEE: *Illustration 191. Playthings*, March 1965.

Mary Poppins and Friends: These dolls are modeled after the characters in the Walt Disney movie, *Mary Poppins*, starring Julie Andrews.

Mary Poppins: plastic body and legs; vinyl arms and head; 12in (31cm); rooted black hair; painted side-glancing eyes with three lashes painted at side of eyes; for clothing see *Illustration 193;* circa 1964-1965.

Michael: plastic body and vinyl head; about 7in (18cm); painted side-glancing eyes; rooted blonde hair; suit has brown pants and deep yellow shirt; blue tie; white collar; knee length socks; circa 1965-1966.

Jane: plastic body and vinyl head; about 7in (18cm); painted side-glancing eyes; rooted blonde hair; deep pink dress with purple trim; purple hair ribbon; knee length socks; circa 1965-1966.

The set came in a gift package.

MARKS: "H" on *Mary's* head; "©9//Horsman Dolls Inc.//6682" on *Michael's* head; "©Horsman Dolls Inc.//6681" on *Jane's* head
SEE: *Illustration 192.* Advertisement in Christmas catalog of Rike's Department Store in Dayton, Ohio.
PRICE: $25-35 (*Mary Poppins*)
$40-45 (*Mary Poppins* in box)
$25-35 (*Michael*, hard to find)
$25-35 (*Jane*, hard to find)
$75-90 (set)
$90-110 (set in gift package)

Mary Poppins: Plastic body; vinyl arms and head; 12in (31cm); black rooted hair; painted side-glancing eyes; three painted eyelashes on each side of eye; doll came with three outfits from the movie, *Mary Poppins,* starring Julie Andrews; Left: outfit worn at night in the nursery — white cotton apron, blue and white striped dress, black stockings and boots; Middle: outfit worn when Mary Poppins "flew" — blue flannel coat, blue felt hat, purple cotton skirt with white bodice, plastic umbrella; Right: outfit worn in the cartoon holiday scene — white dress with pink velvet belt and flowers; white straw hat and netting; 1965.

Mary Poppins also came in 16in (40.6cm) and 26in (66cm) sizes.

   MARKS: None (doll on left); "H" on back of head on the other dolls.
   SEE: *Illustration 193.*
   PRICE: $25-35

Illustration 192.

Illustration 193.

Walt Disney's Cinderella: Plastic body and legs with soft vinyl heads and arms; 11½in (28cm); jointed at neck, shoulders, hips; extra head for "poor" *Cinderella*; blonde rooted hair; painted side-glancing eyes with three eyelashes painted at the corners of eyes on both heads; pierced ears and pink pearl earrings on doll dressed in pink satin ball dress trimmed with silver metallic net sleeves, gloves, peplum; "poor" *Cinderella* dress has yellow skirt, green top, blue sleeves and brown suede weskit; included in the package is a red velvet pillow with glass slipper, pail and mop; black shoes; box has a printed clock with hands almost at midnight, doves flying through the air and instructions, "Midnight...Change Cinderella's head and clothes to her scullery outfit;" 1965.

   1965 was a popular year for Disney dolls and products. Horsman celebrated their "century of quality...1865-1965" with this popular character doll.
   MARKS: "H" (back of both heads)
   SEE: *Illustration 194.*
   PRICE: $90-110 (in box)

Illustration 194.

Patty Duke: Soft poseable vinyl body and head; 12in (31cm); rooted dark blonde hair in a "flip" style with bangs; jointed at shoulders, arms and legs; medium high-heeled doll; painted blue side-glancing eyes with large black pupils; three painted eyelashes at the side of each eye; red lips; fingers molded separately; 3rd and 4th fingers curled; doll represents the actress, Patty Duke, who played twins on her own television show; doll came with autographed picture; telephone; original clothes; gray flannel pants, red sweater trimmed in white; 1965.

MARKS: *Illustration 195.*

PRICE: $45-55 (with picture and telephone)

Illustration 195.

DOLLS NOT PHOTOGRAPHED

Betty: Advertised in Alden's Christmas catalog, 1958; 15in (38cm); came with a trunk and wardrobe.

Little Miss Moppet: Advertised in Montgomery Ward catalog, 1958; 16in (41cm); vinyl; jointed at neck, shoulders, hips; coo voice; wears old fashioned dotted dress; long stockings; high side-buttoned shoes.

Cindy: Advertised in Montgomery Ward catalog, 1958; 25in (64cm) and 36in (91cm); rooted ponytail; jointed at neck, shoulders, hips; bendable knees; individual fingers which could be joined to "pray;" dressed in red and white rayon panties and white nylon pinafore.

Mary Hoyer Doll Mfg. Co.

The registered trademarks, the trademarks and the copyrights appearing in italics within this chapter belong to Mary Hoyer Doll Mfg. Co.

Vicky: Vinyl with soft vinyl head; 10½in (27cm); rooted Saran hair; jointed at shoulders, neck, waist, hips; sleep eyes; dressed in bra and panties; high-heeled sandals; complete wardrobe available from sportswear to formals; pattern and accessories could also be ordered; 1957.

> SEE: *Illustration 196* (top doll in advertisement in *Needlecraft Magazine*).

Illustration 196.

Illustration 197.

Vicky: 12in (31cm); teenage doll with flat heels.

Mary: All plastic; 14in (36cm); fully-jointed; flat heels.

Margie: 10in (25cm); toddler doll.

Cathy: 10in (25cm); baby doll.

By 1965 Mary Hoyer had changed dolls and changed the fashions for the dolls. The outfit for *Vicky* now has the look of a Jacqueline Kennedy fashion. Gone are the full skirts and high heels of the 1957 doll.

> MARKS: *Margie* may have "AE18" on head or body
>
> SEE: *Illustration 197. McCall's Needlework & Crafts*, Fall-Winter, 1965-66.

Ideal Toy Corp.

The registered trademarks, the trademarks and the copyrights appearing in italics within this chapter belong to the Ideal Toy Corp., unless otherwise noted.

In 1957 Ideal published a brochure which proudly proclaimed, "Ideal Toy Corporation's Golden Age of Toys." Today the wonderful dolls from this company are very collectible and mint examples are increasingly hard to find.

The beautiful *Revlon*® high-heeled dolls are pictured on the cover of the brochure in their beautiful full-skirted nylon dresses which were so typical of the high fashion of that period.

The same brochure showed a picture of the new *Shirley Temple* doll modeled after the star who had become newly popular on television. The doll came with many different outfits and costumes from her movies. It caused a sensation among both children and collectors.

In 1960 Ideal advertised in *Playthings*, "What will Ideal think of next?" That year they created the child-sized *Patty Playpal* doll which gave its generic name to the group of large dolls produced by other companies.

In 1962 *Tammy* was introduced to compete in the teen category with *Barbie*®. Little girls wanted both dolls and because *Tammy* was so popular, her family was added to the line. The entire family had a wardrobe, accessories and furniture. The children loved them all. Collectors have discovered that these dolls accurately reflect the family life of that period. They are well-made dolls with beautiful clothing.

In 1965, to compete in the "glamour" market, Ideal created *Glamour Misty* and the *Miss Clairol*® doll. They emphasized the application of makeup.

Many other dolls were also made during this "Golden Age." Ideal's dolls were innovative, followed the fashion trends and personalities, and were well made. They are eagerly sought by collectors.

SEE: *Illustration 198* (Ideal Brochure).

Barbie® is a registered trademark of Mattel, Inc.
Revlon® is a registered trademark of Revlon, Inc.
Clairol® is a registered trademark of Clairol, Inc.

Illustration 198.

Revlon® Dolls: Ideal introduced their full-formed teenage figure dolls in 1955. They were made of vinyl "Magic Touch" skin and were high-heeled. The dolls could bend and turn because of their special swivel waist and could be bathed and powdered. Their rooted Saran hair could be washed and waved. The *Revlon Doll®* was a leader in high fashion clothes and came with elaborate ensembles that included nylons, heels, underwear, jewelry and accessories. This doll came in three sizes: 18in (46cm), 20in (51cm) and 23in (59cm) and was used to advertise and promote the Revlon® Company that sold cosmetics. In 1957 a smaller doll, *Little Miss Revlon®,* was added to their line.

Revlon® Doll: Rigid vinyl body, soft vinyl head; 20in (56cm); swivel waist; high heeled; jointed at neck, shoulders, waist, legs; blue sleep eyes with molded lashes; painted eyelashes under each eye; pierced ears; dark blonde rooted hair that could be combed, washed and curled; feathered eyebrows; red lips, finger and toenails; all fingers molded separately; 3rd and 4th fingers curled; original clothes; blue velveteen dress with pink waist ribbon; tag from dress reads, "Revlon Doll by Ideal"; white fur stole; black and net purse; circa 1957.

> **MARKS:** "IDEAL DOLL/VT 20" (back of head and on doll's back)
> **SEE:** *Illustration 199.*
> **PRICE:** $135-150

Illustration 199.

Revlon Doll®: 18in (46cm); all original in Revlon box; pink and white striped dress; circa 1957-59.

> **MARKS:** "Ideal//VT 18"
> **SEE:** *Illustration 200. Marybeth Manchook Collection.*
> **PRICE:** $125-140

Revlon Doll®: 18in (46cm); short pink glitter dress with puffed sleeves; straw hat; pink high-heeled shoes; circa 1957-1959.

> **MARKS:** "Ideal VT-18"
> **SEE:** *Illustration 201. Marybeth Manchook Collection.*
> **PRICE:** $85-100

Illustration 200.

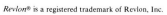

Revlon® is a registered trademark of Revlon, Inc.

Illustration 201.

Revlon Doll Bride®: 18in (46cm); lace dress over tulle underskirt; tulle veil with lace trim; pearl earrings; wedding ring; rose bouquet; circa 1958.

MARKS: "Ideal Doll//VT18"
SEE: *Illustration 202. Marybeth Manchook Collection.*
PRICE: $85-100

Illustration 203.

Illustration 202.

Revlon Doll®: 18in (45.7cm); feathered eyebrows, swivel waist; white nylon dress trimmed with pink lace; a mink stole came with this outfit.

MARKS: "Ideal Doll//VT 18"
SEE: *Illustration 203. Marybeth Manchook Collection.*
PRICE: $85-100

Introduction of *Little Miss Revlon®:* The famous *Revlon®* doll was another "hit" doll for Ideal. In *Toys and Novelties*, February 1957, they introduced a miniature version of the high-heel doll. They advertised that the doll "Had 'Magic Touch' pliable skin, a teen-age figure, pierced ears with pearl earrings, bends at the waist, bows and turns, rooted Saran hair, high heel shoes, eyes open and close, dressed in bra and girdle designed by Formfit." *Little Miss Revlon* had a complete line of clothes including sportswear, formals, pedal pushers, bridal gowns, negligees and outwear.

SEE: *Illustration 204* (doll).
Illustration 205 (clothes).

Illustration 204.

Illustration 205.

Revlon® is a registered trademark of Revlon, Inc.

Illustration 206.

Little Miss Revlon®: See *Illustration 206;* Left doll — turquoise nylon dress with pink flocked flowers trimmed with pink net and braid; dress tagged "Ideal Toy Corp Hollis, N.J."; white lace petticoat; pearl earrings; Right doll — red cotton dress with yellow and green hearts; white nylon pinafore; nylons; red purse and shoes; pearl earrings; circa 1958.

MARKS: "IDEAL DOLL/VT 10½" (head)

SEE: *Illustration 207.*

PRICE: $60-70 (in box)
$45-60 (doll)
$20-35 (for boxed outfits)

Illustration 208.

Little Miss Revlon®: Vinyl "Magic Touch" pliable skin, soft vinyl head; 10½in (27cm); high heeled; rooted dark blonde hair pulled back in ponytail; hair could be combed, washed and curled; swivel waist; jointed at neck, shoulders, waist and legs; blue sleep eyes; five painted eyelashes at side of each eye; pierced ears; red lips, finger and toenails; arched brown eyebrows; advertising doll for *Revlon®* beauty and cosmetic company; boxed fashion outfits could be purchased separately; 1957.

MARKS: "IDEAL DOLL/VT 10½" (head); "10½ R" (arm under shoulder)

SEE: *Illustration 206.*

PRICE: $60-70 (in box)
$45-60 (doll)
$20-35 (boxed outfit)

Illustration 207.

Little Miss Revlon®: See *Illustration 206;* Left doll — dark brown curly rooted hair; red cotton dress with red and green plaid scarf and tam; black belt and purse; nylons; red shoes; Right doll — cocktail dress of dotted Swiss nylon; yellow layered skirt and turquoise bodice; turquoise waist ribbon and Ideal tag on outside of dress; circa 1958.

MARKS: "IDEAL DOLL/VT 10½" (head)

SEE: *Illustration 208.*

PRICE: $45-60

Illustration 210.

Little Miss Revlon® Brochure from left to right:

Illustration 210 top row:
1. Description of doll; *Little Miss Revlon's* Big Sister

bottom row:
1. Negligee Set
2. Hostess Gown

SCHOOL SERIES
3. Torso Dress
4. School Dress

BRIDAL SERIES
5. Bridal
6. Bridesmaid Outfit
7. Debutante Bridal Gown

COATS
8. Flared Woolen Coat

Illustration 211 top row:
1. Party Dress
2. School Dress

PLAYTIME SERIES
3. 2-piece Playsuit
4. Sundress and Bonnet
5. Velvet Sheath
6. 5-piece Redingote Outfit
7. Princess Style Outfit
8. Striped Suit with Hat

bottom row:
JUNIOR MISS SERIES
1. Skirt and Blouse
2. Sweater and Skirt
3. Pinafore
4. Pinafore

NOVELTY SERIES
5. Sailor Outfit
6. Ballerina
7. Calypso Blouse and Skirt
8. Nurse Outfit

Illustration 212 top row:
FORMAL SERIES
1. Lace Formal
2. Taffeta Formal
3. Nylon Formal
4. Debutante Formal
5. Polka Dot Dress
6. Jumper
7. Striped Dress
8. Gay Stripe Dress

bottom row:
1. Artist's Outfit

VISITING OUTFITS
2. Visiting Outfit
3. Traveling Outfit
4. Sunday Outfit
5. Pedal Pusher Outfit
6. Jeans and Shirt
7. Sunsuit
8. Coolie Beach Outfit

Illustration 213
1. Raincoat, Boots, Tote Bag
2. Checked Coat, Hat, Purse

BOXED SETS
3. *Little Miss Revlon* Gift Box
4. *Little Miss Revlon* Travel Case;
   NIGHT TIME SERIES
5. Shorty Nightgown
6. Pajamas
7. Lounging Pajamas
8. TV Lounging Outfit

Revlon® is a registered trademark of Revlon, Inc.

Illustration 211.

Illustration 212.

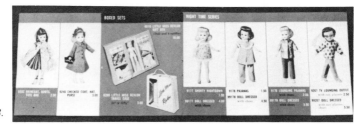

Illustration 213.

Shirley Temple: In their 1957 "Golden Age of Toys" brochure, Ideal published this picture of their *Shirley Temple* doll complete with her famous polka dot party dress. The actress, Shirley Temple, was featured at that time in a revival of her movies which were appearing on television.

SEE: *Illustration 214. Ideal brochure*, 1957.
PRICE: $180+

Shirley Temple Doll and Shirley Temple Black: Shirley Temple attended the New York Toy Fair in February 1958. She is pictured with a vinyl *Shirley Temple* doll which is completely washable. There were 13 outfits available for sale.

   SEE: *Illustration 215. Toys and Novelties*, May 1958.

Shirley Temple from left to right:
1. Rigid vinyl with soft vinyl face; hazel eyes with molded lashes; 12in (31cm); blonde dark curly rooted hair; open-mouth with six teeth; dressed in ice skating costume with tagged red knit top with blue and white anchor patch; black velvet skirt with red and white checked lining; gold elastic at waist; skates not original; 1957-1959.
2. Rigid vinyl; 15in (38cm); blonde curly rooted hair; hazel sleep eyes with real lashes; open-mouth with six teeth; feathered eyebrows; painted eyelashes below eyes; blue nylon dress with white lace and pink satin ribbon trim; tiny embroidered flowers on collar and waist; all original including shoes; circa 1957-1959.
3. Same characteristics as doll #1; 12in (31cm); yellow nylon dress trimmed with nylon lace; silver "Shirley" pin on satin sash; dress tagged "Shirley Temple//Made by Ideal Toy Corporation"; shoes not original; circa 1957-1959.
   MARKS: from left to right:
   1. "Ideal Doll//ST 12" (head); none on body
   2. "Ideal Doll//ST-15N" (head); none on body
   3. "Ideal Doll//ST 12" (head); "ST-12-N" (back)
   SEE: *Illustration 216.*
   PRICE: 12in (31cm) $120-130
   15in (38cm) $200-220 (all original in mint condition)

SHIRLEY TEMPLE DOLL. An authentic reproduction of the famous curly haired child star who is now back on TV in your favorite Shirley Temple movies. Doll features all washable "magic touch" skin. Dressed in attractive outfit complete with party dress, petticoat and vinyl shoes. Her famous golden curls are made of the finest rooted Saran hair. This is the "real" Shirley Temple—from her hazel eyes to the adorable dimpled cheeks. $11.95 and up.

Illustration 214.

Illustration 216.

Illustration 215.

Shirley Temple in red coat: 12in (31cm); for general characteristics, see *Illustration 216,* unusual red flannel coat, tam and muff. The lovely coat was made by one of leading makers of women's and children's coats in the United States, Bambury. They also made coats for *Tweedie®,* a Horsman doll.

> **MARKS:** "Shirley Temple// Miniature//by Bambury" (tag inside coat)
> **SEE:** *Illustration 217. Private Collection.*
> **PRICE:** $60 (coat)

Illustration 217

960—Shirley Temple steps out of the movies—into your little girl's heart! 12" Ideal doll in petticoat and panties to dress in a variety of costumes. **3.98**
Outfits only, to purchase separately:
960A—Wee Willie Winkie Scotch outfit. **3.00**
960B—Pinafore party outfit. **2.00**
960C—Sailor suit with beret, shoes, socks. **1.50**

Illustration 218.

Shirley Temple: Vinyl; 36in (91cm); wears three-year-old dresses; blonde rooted Saran curls that can be shampooed and set; hazel eyes; dimpled cheeks; 1960.

> **SEE:** *Illustration 219. Toys and Novelties,* February 1960.
> **PRICE:** $1200-1300+ (mint-in-box)

Shirley Temple: Rigid vinyl; 12in (31cm); these outfits could be purchased separately; doll was available in just petticoat and panties. *Wee Willie Winkie* Scotch outfit; pinafore party dress; sailor dress with beret, shoes and socks; 1959.

> **MARKS:** "IDEAL DOLL//ST-12" (head); "ST-12" (body)
> **SEE:** *Illustration 218.* Newspaper advertisement for Christmas, 1959.

SHIRLEY TEMPLE DOLL is three foot high and wears three year old dresses. She has blonde, rooted Saran curls that can be shampooed and set, hazel eyes and dimpled cheeks. $39.95 retail. Ideal Toy, 200 Fifth ave., New York.

Illustration 219.

Tweedie® is a registered trademark of Horsman Dolls, Inc.

Illustration 220.   *Illustration 221.*   *Illustration 222.*

Tammy: Vinyl head and arms; plastic legs and body; 12in (31cm); jointed at neck, shoulders, hips; painted side-glancing eyes; three painted eyelashes at corners of eyes; rooted blonde hair; doll on left is dressed in bright red ski outfit with hood, ski poles and skis; doll on right is dressed in *Cutie Co-ed* outfit which has a bright red sweater and leotard; blue corduroy jumper; red tote bag; radio; 1962. The first *Tammy* came with a plastic stand that gripped the ankles.

Early case has skis, *Cutie Co-ed* and *Model Miss* outfits on top; *Tammy* came with an extensive wardrobe which could be purchased separately.

> **MARKS:** "© Ideal Toy Corp.//B5-12" (head); "© Ideal Toy Corp.//B5-12½" (body)
> **SEE:** *Illustration 220.*
> **PRICE:** $30-50 (depending on costume)

Ted (Tammy's brother), Tammy, Pos'n Tammy from left to right:
Ted: Vinyl head and arms, plastic legs and body; 12½in (32cm); jointed at neck, shoulders, hips; painted side-glancing eyes; dressed in blue pajamas; 1963. *Pos'n Ted* was added in 1964; *Dad* and *Ted* could share their wardrobes.
Tammy: For general characteristics and marks, see *Illustration 220;* pink pajama tops with pantaloon bottoms.
Pos'n Tammy: For general characteristics and marks, see *Illustration 222;* white shorts with blue striped shirt.

> **MARKS:** Ted: "© Ideal Toy Corp.//B-12-1/2-W-2" (head); "© Ideal Toy Corp.//B-12-1/2" (body)
> **SEE:** *Illustration 221.*
> **PRICE:** $30-50 (depending on costume)

Pos'n Tammy and her Telephone Booth (No. 9105-8): Poseable vinyl; 12in (31cm); rooted hair; painted eyes with four eyelash lines at side of eye; individual fingers; closed-mouth; bubble cut hair with long ponytail attached; red knit jump suit with white bow and collar; vinyl tennis shoes; all original; 1965.

> **MARKS:** "Ideal Toy Corp.//BS 12" (head); "Ideal Toy Corp//BS12//1" (back)
> **SEE:** *Illustration 222.*
> **PRICE:** $60

Misty: See *Illustration 224* for general characteristics.

Grown-up Tammy: Vinyl head and arms, plastic body and legs; 11¾in (30cm); came with stand that fit into a plastic band around the waist; painted side-glancing eyes; three lashes at corners of eyes; shoes had slight heels; each outfit came with makeup for the occasion; 1965.

Grown-up Tammy also came as *Grown Up Pos'n Tammy*. Both had the same marks.

MARKS: "©1964//Ideal Toy Corp//T-12-E" (head); "©1965//Ideal//T-12" (right hip)

SEE: *Illustration 223. Playthings*, September 1965.

Glamour Misty The Miss Clairol® Doll: Plastic body and legs; rigid vinyl non-poseable arms; soft vinyl head; 12in (31cm); blonde rooted hair; painted side-glancing eyes with heavy black eyeliner; heavy blue eye shadow above eyes; jointed at neck, shoulders, hips; high-heeled shoes; pink lace-trimmed bra and panties with pink net short negligee; can wear *Tammy* clothes; boxed set came with three non-toxic hair applicators in red, yellow and brown; white print terry cloth cover-up; yellow comb; 1965.

MARKS: "©1965//Ideal in Oval//M-12" (above right leg); "Ideal Toy Corp.//W-12-3" (head)

SEE: *Illustration 224.*

PRICE: $75+ (boxed set)

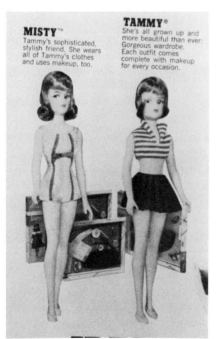

Illustration 223.

Illustration 224.

Clairol® is a registered trademark of Clairol, Inc.

Illustration 225.   *Illustration 226.*   *Illustration 227.*

Mom and Dad (part of Tammy's family).

Mom: Vinyl head and arms; plastic legs and torso; 12½in (32cm); jointed at neck, shoulders, hips; painted side-glancing eyes; rooted hair done in a "French twist"; blue print sheath dress; high-heeled shoes; *Mom* came with her wardrobe which could be purchased separately; *Mom* could also wear *Tammy's* clothes; 1963.

Dad: Vinyl head and arms; plastic legs and torso; 13in (33cm); jointed at neck, shoulders, hips; painted side-glancing eyes; molded painted brown hair; red and white striped sports shirt and black slacks; *Dad* and *Ted, Tammy's* brother, wore interchangeable clothes that could be purchased separately; 1963.

    MARKS: *Mom:* "© Ideal Toy Corp.//W-13-L" (head); "© Ideal Toy Corp.//W-13" (body)

             Dad: "© Ideal Toy Corp.//M 13 2" (head); "© Ideal toy Corp.//B-12-1/2" (body)

    SEE: *Illustration 225.*

    PRICE: $30-50

Pepper: Vinyl head and arms; plastic legs and torso; 9¼in (24cm); jointed at neck, shoulders, hips; painted side-glancing eyes; three painted eyelashes at corners of each eye; freckles around nose; rooted hair; yellow ballerina dress trimmed with flowers on doll at left; dress with blue and white striped skirt, blue top with white trim on doll on right; 1963-64.

    MARKS: Left doll: "© Ideal Toy Corp.//G9-W" (head); "© Ideal Toy Corp. G9-W//1" (back); Right doll: "© Ideal Toy Corp.//G9-W (head); "© Ideal Toy Corp. G9-W//2" (back)

    SEE: *Illustration 226.*

    PRICE: $30-45 (in box)

Pos'n Pepper: Vinyl head, arms, legs; plastic body; 9¼in (24cm); blonde rooted hair; painted eyes with three lashes at the side of each eye; arms lift together; flat feet; short hairdo; freckles under eyes; shown in box sitting on a swing; original dress; red cotton skirt with a knit multi-colored striped top; 1964.

    MARKS: "© Ideal Toy Corp.//G9-E" (head); © Ideal Toy Corp.//G-9-W//1" (back); "Pepper//Ideal//Japan" (tag on dress)

    SEE: *Illustration 227.*

    PRICE: $30-45

New Pepper: Vinyl head, arms, plastic legs and body; 9¼in (24cm); a little slimmer than 1963 *Pepper;* rooted hair; painted side-glancing eyes; three lashes at corners of eyes; red and white playsuit; flat feet.

Dodi: Same body as *New Pepper;* different heads; markings vary slightly; blue felt jumper and red sweater; 1965.

> MARKS: *New Pepper:* "©1965// Ideal Toy Corp.//P9-3"(head); "1964©//Ideal//2 DO-9"(hip)
> MARKS: *Dodi:* "©1964//Ideal Toy Corp.//DO-9-E" (head); "1964 ©//Ideal//1 DO-9//1" (back)
> SEE: *Illustration 228. Playthings,* September 1965.
> PRICE: $25-35 (either doll)

Illustration 228.

Pepper and Dodi: For general characteristics and marks for both dolls, see *Illustration 228. Pepper,* left, is wearing a white hooded sweatshirt printed with school numbers and letters. *Dodi,* right, has a white tennis dress covered with a white tennis sweater.

> SEE: *Illustration 229.*
> PRICE: $25-35

Pos'n Salty: Vinyl arms, legs; soft vinyl head; plastic body; 7¾in (20cm); brown painted eyes; brown painted hair; freckled; wears red pants with striped tee shirt; accessories include a baseball, bat, cap, catcher's mask; 1964.

 The same doll was used for both *Tammy's Little Brother Pete* and *Pepper's Friend Salty. Pete* was dressed in patched jeans with shirts of several different colors. Both dolls had the same markings.

> MARKS: "©1964//Ideal Toy Corp." (head); "©1964//Ideal Toy Corporation" (back)
> SEE: *Illustration 230. Phyllis Parr Collection.*
> PRICE: $40-50

Illustration 229.

Illustration 230.

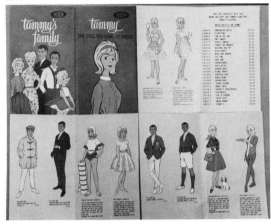

Illustration 231.

Tammy Brochure from left to right:
1. Cover pages.
2. *Underwear Outfits; Sleepytime.*
3. *Ted and Dad: Sports Car Coat and Cap; Two-button Suit; Jacket; Trousers; Shoes.*
   Tammy: Fun in the Sun; Knit Knack.
4. *Ted and Dad: Blazer Jacket; Cardigan Sweater and Matching High Socks.*
   Tammy: Walking Her Pet; Pizza Party.
   SEE: *Illustration 231.*

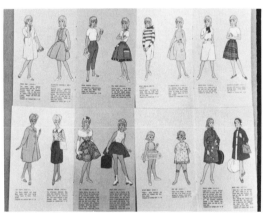

Illustration 232.

Tammy Brochure from left to right:
1. *Tammy: Pin Checked Housecoat; Sleeveless Shirtwaist Dress; Pedal Pushers; Full Skirt with Fringe.*
2. *Tammy: Heavy Woolen Striped Sweater; Afternoon Dress; White Sheath Dress; Pleated Plaid Skirt.*
3. *Tammy: Lazy Days Brunch Coat; Shopping Dress; Fur 'N Formal; Skate Date.*
4. *Pepper: Nylon Undies; Bed Time Pajamas.*
   Tammy: Travel Checked Shift; Model Miss.
   SEE: *Illustration 232.*

Illustration 233.

Tammy Brochure from left to right:
1. The *Tammy* Family: *Tammy, Pepper, Dad, Ted* and *Mom.*
2. Check list for clothes for *Mom* and *Pepper* which could be purchased on a card.
3. *Tammy: Puddle Jumper Raincoat; Tennis the Menace.*
   Ted and *Dad: Sports Vest, Tie and Shoes; Sweater and Slack Outfit.*
4. *Tammy: Beau and Arrow Archery Set; Tee Time Golf Clothes.*
   Ted and *Dad: Bathrobe and Slippers; Pullover Sweater.*
   SEE: *Illustration 233.*

Illustration 234.

Tammy Brochure from left to right:
1. *Tammy: Short Sleeved Blouse; Long Sleeved Blouse; Plaid Jumper; Sleeveless Sweater.*
2. *Tammy: Sleeveless Blouse; Slacks; Shorty Nightgown; Sheath Dress.*
3. *Tammy: Snow Bunny Ski Outfit; Figure 8 Ice Skating Outfit.*
   Mom: Nighty Nite; Hidden Glamor Underwear.
4. *Tammy: Sorority Sweetheart Skirt, Jerkin, Blouse; Checkmate Blazer, Pleated Skirt; Blouse.*
   Mother: Evening in Paris Short Formal; Lounging Luxury Blouse, Slacks.
   SEE: *Illustration 234.*

Illustration 235.   *Illustration 236.*

Tammy Brochure from left to right:

1. *Ring-a-Ding:* ruffled blouse; black velvet pants; wedgie shoes; Princess phone.
2. *Dream Boat:* date dress in blue brocade and satin; embossed silk jacket; flowered headband; medium-heeled shoes; gold purse; date book; camera.
3. *Pepper's Classroom Caper:* school dress with flared skirt and embroidered waistband; lace-trimmed panties.
4. *Pepper's After School Fun:* knitted wool sweater; elastic-topped slacks.
   SEE: *Illustration 235.*

Tammy Brochure upper row from left to right:

1. *Ted* and *Dad*: Bermuda shorts and high socks.
2. *Ted* and *Dad*: pajamas and slippers.
3. *Purl One:* tailored sleeveless shirtwaist dress that buttons down the front; red and black shoulder bag; checked hankie; knitting bag with wool; knitting needles; medium-heeled shoes.
4. *Cheerleader outfit:* bulky white sweater with letter "T"; short red flared felt skirt; matching cap with chin strap; high socks with white sneakers; baton; megaphone.

Lower row from left to right:

1. *Pepper:* flannel winter coat with simulated fur; matching headband.
2. *Pepper:* nylon and velvet party dress; pearls.
3. *Picnic Party:* striped knit shirt; clam digger pants; sneakers; sunglasses; headband; picnic basket.
4. *Sweater Girl:* red cardigan sweater with push-up sleeves; gray sheath skirt; two-strand necklace matches buttons on sweater; camera; purse; eyeglasses; date book; style book.
   SEE: *Illustration 236.*

Tammy Family Dolls Not Photographed:

Black Tammy: Vinyl head and arms; plastic legs and body; 11¾in (30cm); jointed at neck, shoulders, hips; 1964-1965.

    MARKS: "©1964//Ideal Toy Corp.//T-12-E" (head); "©1965//Ideal//T-12" (body)

Patti, Pepper's Playmate: Vinyl head and arms; plastic legs and body; 9¼in (24cm); jointed at neck, shoulders, hips; 1964.

    MARKS: "© Ideal Toy Corp.//G9-L" (head); "© Ideal Toy Corp.//G-9-W" (body)

Bud, Tammy's Boyfriend: Vinyl head and arms; plastic legs and body; 12½in (32cm); jointed at neck, shoulders, hips; 1964-1965.

    MARKS: "©1964//Ideal Toy Corp.//T8 12-W-2" (head); "© Ideal Toy Corp//B 12½//2" (body)

Illustration 237.

The Family of Play Pals: Advertised as made of indestructible plastics; sculptured according to U.S. Bureau of Standards specifications. They could wear the actual clothing of a child at that age. They are very lightweight for dolls of their size. The following dolls were in the 1960 line:

1. *Suzy Play Pal* — as big as a one-year-old girl.
2. *Johnny Play Pal* — as big as a three-month-old baby boy.
3. *Bonnie Play Pal* — as big as a three-month old baby girl.
4. *Penny Play Pal* — as big as a two-year-old girl.
5. *Patti Play Pal* — as big as a three-year-old girl; has straight hair.
6. *Patti Play Pal* — as big as a three-year-old girl; has curly hair.

    SEE: *Illustration 237. Toys and Novelties*, May 1960.

Illustration 238.

Patti Playpal: Unusually light hollow plastic body with soft vinyl head; 36in (91cm); straight rooted brunette hair; feathered eyebrows; sleep eyes; size of a three-year-old child; excellent skin tone; 3rd and 4th fingers molded together and curled inward; excellent quality large doll; dressed in red dress with nylon apron; patent leather shoes with strap; all original; circa 1960.

> **MARKS:** "IDEAL//DOLL// G35" (head)
> **SEE:** *Illustration 238. Beatrice Campbell Collection.*
> **PRICE:** $140-160

Patti Playpal: Vinyl; 36in (91cm); became a walking doll in 1960; a new wardrobe was designed for *Patti* this year and a name tag was added to each dress.

> **SEE:** *Illustration 239. Toys and Novelties,* May 1960.

PATTI PLAYPAL has a new wardrobe. The three-foot-high doll, in one of her new costumes, has been redesigned this year and now has a walking mechanism. Each dress now has Patti's name on it. $30. Ideal Toy, 200 Fifth ave., N.Y.

Illustration 239.

Patti Playpal: 36in (91cm); light plastic; see general characteristics; reddish rooted hair; original clothes; white pinafore over laced-trimmed gingham blouse; black patent shoes; circa 1960.

MARKS: "Ideal Doll//G-35" on back of neck;c//"Ideal Toy Corp//G-35-7" on back

SEE: *Illustration 240. Inga Tomoletz Collection.*

PRICE: $250-275

Illustration 240.

Illustration 241.

Peter Playpal: Rigid vinyl; 38in (97cm); fully-jointed; could wear little boys' clothing; companion to *Patty Playpal*; dressed in short dark blue pants, blue shirt, red knee socks; circa 1960-61.

MARKS: "Ideal Toy Corp//B35-38" (head); "Ideal Toy Corp.// W-38//Pat. Pend" (body)

SEE: *Illustration 241. Trudy Vasiloff Collection.*

PRICE: $200-250 (depending on all original outfit)

Illustration 242a.

Mitzi: Vinyl; 12in (31cm); *Barbie®* look-alike; several colors of hair; eyes painted; high-heeled feet; came dressed in box in two-piece bathing suit; has round stand; doll in illustration dressed in strapless gold sheath dress with black net round hem; circa 1960-1961.

> **MARKS:** "Ideal Toy Corp.// 1960//2."
> **SEE:** *Illustration 242b. Elsie E. Ogden Collection.*
> **PRICE:** $35-45 (depending on outfit)

Betsy McCall®: Hollow light plastic body and soft vinyl head; 36in (91cm); jointed at neck, shoulders, hips; sleep eyes; red check skirt with suspenders of the same material; white blouse; jewelry not original; 1959.

> **MARKS:** "McCall Corp/©/ 1959" (back of body)
> **SEE:** *Illustration 242a. Thelma Purvis Collection.*
> **PRICE:** $225-245+

Illustration 242b.

Illustration 243.

Little Princess Doll House Dolls: Hard plastic; father 6in (15cm); mother 5½in (14cm); boy 4in (10cm); girl 3¾in (10cm); jointed at neck, arms, hips; painted eyes; mother and girl have wigs; father and boy have molded hair; Mother has white skirt and blue and white printed blouse; girl has red dress and shoes; boy has red sweater and black pants (He does not have striped shirt like the catalog); father has gray pants and black suitcoat; picture from 1964 Ideal wholesale toy catalog. Marx made a similar family set (see *Illustration 265*); 1964.

> **MARKS:** All the clothes of the dolls are tagged "© Ideal//Hong Kong"
> **SEE:** *Illustration 243. Dorothy Hesner Collection.*
> **PRICE:** $50 and up (rare)

DOLLS NOT PHOTOGRAPHED

Daddy's Girl: Plastic body and soft vinyl head; 42in (107cm) and 36in (91cm); rooted blonde hair; sleep eyes with lashes; closed smiling mouth; jointed at neck, shoulders, waist, hips, ankles; 1960.

In 1960 there were technical advances which allowed the creation of these very large dolls. (See *Illustration 429.*)

> **PRICE:** $125-145

Jackie Look-Alike: Plastic with vinyl head; 16in (41cm); circa 1961.

> **MARKS:** "Ideal Toy Corp//G 15L" (head); "Ideal Corp.//M15" (back)

Girl: One-piece stuffed vinyl head and body; 17in (43cm); circa 1957.

> **MARKS:** "Ideal Doll//VP-17-Z" (head); "Ideal Doll//P17//0" (body)
> **PRICE:** $80-100

Lori Martin: Hard plastic body with soft vinyl head; 38in (97cm); closed smiling mouth; jointed at neck, shoulders, waist, hips, ankles; a few were jointed at wrists; circa 1961.

This doll is from the film *National Velvet*.

> **MARKS:** "Metro-Goldwyn-Mayer, Inc.//Mfg.//Ideal Toy Corp//38" (head)
> **PRICE:** $100-135

Samantha the Witch: Plastic with soft vinyl head; 12in (31cm); *Barbie*®-type; rooted white hair; green eyes; circa 1965.

> **MARKS:** "Ideal Toy Corp.//M-12E 2" (head); "1965//Ideal//M-12 (in oval)" (hip)

Barbie® is a registered trademark of Mattel, Inc.

Juro Novelty Co., Inc.

Juro dolls were popular during the 1955 to 1965 period and widely advertised on television. They featured celebrity and personality dolls, and they were well-known for their ventriloquist dolls. They also had girl ventriloquist dolls. Among their other dolls were the popular high-heeled dolls. These were often used as "giveaways" when merchandise was purchased.

The personality dolls advertised in *Playthings*, March 1955, featured Arthur Murray's Original Dancing Dolls and Bill Baird's Puppets.

SEE: *Illustration 244.*

Rags to Riches Doll: Vinyl; 14in (36cm) and 20in (51cm); jointed at neck, shoulders, waist, hips; white dress with royal blue long bow; white crown with rhinestones; high-heeled feet; "poor" dress patched together cotton print with light blue scarf for head; circa 1957.

This doll was given away by a local furniture company in Cleveland, Ohio, with the purchase of a cedar chest.

MARKS: None on doll
SEE: *Illustration 245. Dolly Jakubecz Collection.*
PRICE: $45-50 (complete)

Illustration 244.　　　　　　　Illustration 245.

DOLLS NOT PHOTOGRAPHED

Dick Clark: Autograph doll; cloth body; molded vinyl portrait-type head and hands; 26in (66cm); original clothes included suede saddle shoes; yellow vest, dark gray trousers; light gray jacket, white shirt, red plaid tie; autograph pen included; 1958-1959.

Dick Clark's "Bandstand" program on early television was a favorite of the teenage set. Students came home from school to watch this program, and they copied the styles of the boys and girls. Girls wore either a long straight skirt or a full skirt with crinolines and hoop. These were combined with black flats with stockings or white sneakers with socks. The students from Philadelphia on the program set the style standards for the generation.

MARKS: "Juro" (body); "Juro Novelty Co., Inc. NYC//Another Celebrity Doll" (box)

Kaysam-Jolly Toy Corporation

The registered trademarks, the trademarks and the copyrights appearing in italics within this chapter belong to Kaysam-Jolly Toy Corporation.

The high-heeled fashion dolls from this company were often marked "Kaysam" on the doll but sometimes had a tag with "Jolly Company" on it. They made slender, rather mature dolls who wore high-fashion clothes. The Ice Capades used some of their dolls for their costume designs.

Another of their interesting dolls was the *Hello Dolly* doll which was modeled after Carol Channing. It has a Kaysam mark on its head, but the box is marked "Nasco." (See Nasco section, page 321.)

Illustration 246.

Illustration 247.

Advertisement "You have a date with a 'living doll'": Jolly toys advertised their dolls in *Playthings*, March 1962, as having "...beauty, glamour, and a wealth of original innovations."

SEE: *Illustration 246.*

Girl with High-Heels: Rigid vinyl body with soft vinyl head; 21in (53cm); pink nylon dress; 1961.

MARKS: "1961" (under hair on head); "Kaysam Corp." (lower head).

SEE: *Illustration 247. M. Catherine Lawrence Collection.*

PRICE: $25-35

DOLLS NOT PHOTOGRAPHED

This company made many high-heeled, matured-figure dolls of various sizes. They used such names as *Catherine, June Bride, Red Cross Nurse, Jackie* and *Cynthia.* They also made personality dolls.

Gigi (Juliet Prowse): Plastic and vinyl; rooted hair; sleep eyes with eye shadow; red taffeta dress, white bloomers, black garter with red rose; circa 1961.

MARKS: "Kaysam, 1961"

Kenner

The registered trademarks, the trademarks and the copyrights appearing in italics within this chapter belong to Kenner.

Illustration 248.

Katie: 6in (15cm); mold and put together with Electric Mold Master; movable arms and legs; can be dressed with patterns and material included in set; advertising says, "Make all of Katie's accessories, wigs, hats, high-heel shoes, also their suitcases, radios, telephones, guitars, etc...and jewelry for yourself too!"; molds for all are included; 1964.

> **SEE:** *Illustration 248. Toys and Novelties*, September 1964.

Laurel Dolls, Inc.

The registered trademarks, the trademarks and the copyrights appearing in italics within this chapter belong to Laurel Dolls, Inc.

Laurel Dolls, Inc. advertised that their newest doll sensations could talk by "Pulling the string and see the lips move as they talk."

Penny the Fashion Doll: Soft vinyl head; 25in (64cm); high heeled; fashion clothes.

Gabby Baby: Vinyl; soft vinyl head; 20in (51cm); talking; rooted hair.

Gabby Jane: Vinyl; soft vinyl head; 24in (61cm); walking; talking; rooted hair.

Gabby Linda: Soft vinyl head; 20in (51cm); rooted hair; talking.

All dolls available in white or black. Spanish speaking dolls also available in all models.

> **SEE:** *Illustration 249. Toys and Novelties*, April 1962.
>
> **PRICE:** $55-75 (*Penny*)
> $35-45 (*Gabby*)
> $55-75 (*Gabby Jane*)
> $50-65 (*Gabby Linda*)
> (more if Spanish-speaking doll)

Illustration 249.

Lilli (Bild Lilli of Germany)

The registered trademarks, the trademarks and the copyrights appearing in italics within this chapter belong to Bild Lilli, unless otherwise noted.

In the early 1950s a cartoon character named Lilli was created in Hamburg in a German newspaper called Bild. She was a curvaceous blonde with a ponytail tied with a vinyl string-type bow. She was dressed in the latest fashion.

Soon a beautiful doll named *Lilli* appeared on the German market. She was made of a light hard plastic with a beautiful skin tone. The eyes were black and white and heavily lined. She had black molded eyelashes and light gray mascara. Her black high-heeled shoes were molded and painted as were her black flowered earrings.

Fully-jointed, she was strung and her arm hooks are similar to *Muffie's*®. (See *Hard Plastic Dolls*, page 263.)

Most of the *Lilli* dolls are blonde like the original cartoon character. However, they did make a doll with deep auburn hair and another with dark brunette hair. (See *Illustrations 251* and *253*.) The hair was inserted into the top of the head and a type of "spit curl" was hung down over the forehead.

The doll came in two sizes, 11½in (29cm) and 7½in (19cm). Both sizes were dressed in the high fashion for the adults of the period. This fashion was unusual for German dolls. Today these original *Lilli* dolls are hard-to-find.

SEE: *Illustration 250. Sandy Goss Collection.*

Illustration 250.

Lilli: Hard plastic; 11½in (29cm); unusually fine quality and color; fully-jointed; both shoes have holes but only the right one has a prong; four fingers molded together with thumb separate; eye blusher above eyes; molded flower earrings painted black; deep auburn hair; puckered mouth; red dress with bouffant skirt and big bow in back; molded painted high-heeled shoes with large square heel.

This doll was purchased in 1956 at Marshall Field & Company in Chicago, Illinois, by its owner. No separate clothes were sold but there were other models of the doll with different outfits. Mrs. Hesner chose the doll with auburn hair because it was similar to her own. She also liked the beautiful red dress. The dress has a gripper type fastener. (see *Illustration 255*.)

Muffie® is a registered trademark of Nancy Ann Storybook Dolls Co.

MARKS: No marks on body; "Lilli" (printed on base); "Germany" (stamped on bottom of base)

SEE: *Illustration 251* (doll with stand). *Dorothy Hesner Collection.*

Illustration 252 (doll body with foot prong). *Dorothy Hesner Collection.*

PRICE: $600-700 (blonde doll) Not enough samples available to price the auburn and brunette dolls.

Illustration 251.

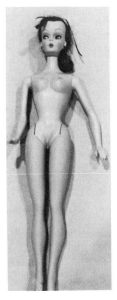

Illustration 252.

Illustration 253.

Lilli: For general characteristics, see *Illustrations 250* and *251.* This belongs to Stefanie Deutsch of West Germany. She reports that she purchased this doll from a lady who played with it as a child. Her original clothes include slacks, a top and jacket. The doll has the original mini "Bild" newspaper under her arm.

Stefanie is president of the *Barbie®* collector club for Germany, Austria and Switzerland. Her collection is being exhibited in 1988 and 1989 in the large shopping centers in Switzerland.

SEE: *Illustration 253. Stefanie Deutsch Collection.*

Barbie® is a registered trademark of Mattel, Inc.

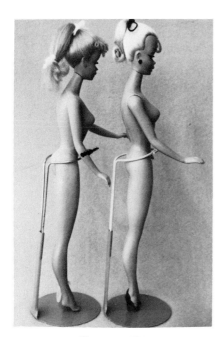

Illustration 254.

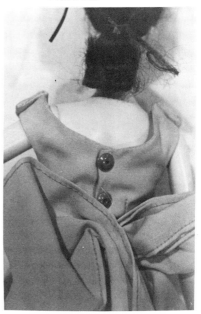

Illustration 255.

Comparison of Lilli and Barbie®: Although both dolls are very similar, there are differences in their sculptured figures. *Barbie®* is on the left. *Lilli* is on the right.

> **SEE:** *Illustration 254.* Both dolls are from the *Sandy Goss Collection.*

Lilli: Close-up of gripper snap which fastens the original *Lilli* red dress. Also seen is the large bow of the same material as the dress.

> **SEE:** *Illustration 255. Dorothy Hesner Collection.*

Lilli Look-Alikes

Soon after *Lilli* was made in Germany, several companies began to make similar dolls in Hong Kong. Collectors now call these dolls *Hong Kong Lillis.* They were among the first dolls to be manufactured there.

Marx was one of the early companies to make dolls in Hong Kong and they are known to have made look-alike dolls of this period.

Another company who made look-alike dolls in Hong Kong was the Faber Luft Ltd. (Also known as Fab-Lu Limited. See page 105.) They often marked their dolls with a "F" in a square. Some of the *Lilli* look-alikes have this marking. Over the years there have been many imitations of *Lilli* and *Barbie®* made in Hong Kong.

Today these dolls have become very collectible and some of them are made of excellent material. Some have beautiful wardrobes. It is difficult to find them mint-in-box.

Hong Kong Lilli: Light hard plastic; 11½in (29cm); fully-jointed; very long neck; unusual hip joint; heavy molded eyelids; white irises similar to first *Barbie®*; unusual eyebrows; cutout scalp with inset hair; "spit curl" on forehead; blonde ponytail; molded painted high-heeled shoes with holes for stand on bottom; dressed in original blue dress which has turned pink; dress similar to *Lilli's* except that it has regular snaps instead of gripper snaps; *Lilli's* dress is of better quality (see *Illustration 251*); clothes all original. This doll was purchased by its owner in October 1958.

> MARKS: "F" in a square//
> "Made in Hong Kong"(on back
> close to waistline)
> SEE: *Illustration 256* (dressed doll
> on stand). *Dorothy Hesner
> Collection.*
> PRICE: $50-70

Illustration 256.

Illustration 257.

Hong Kong Lilli: Excellent quality shiny hard plastic; 12in (31cm); blue irises in eyes; molded eyelashes; unpainted eyebrows; jointed at neck, shoulders, hips, elongated neck; blonde ponytail; fingers molded together with separate thumb; high-heeled feet with painted-on shoes; molded unpainted earrings; clothes not original; circa 1957-1961.

This is almost a line-by-line copy of the German *Lilli*. Even the shoes and earrings are molded like *Lilli*.

> MARKS: "F" in a square//
> "Made in Hong Kong// (on
> back near waist)
> SEE: *Illustration 257.*
> PRICE: $50-70

Barbie® is a registered trademark of Mattel, Inc.

Illustration 258.

Illustration 259.

Hong Kong Lilli: Hard plastic; 7½in (19cm); unusual thread hair ponytail; fully-jointed; holes in feet for stand; original shorts and halter top; 1958-1959.
    MARKS: "Made in Hong Kong" (on back under halter top)
    SEE: *Illustration 258. Dorothy Hesner Collection.*
    PRICE: $35-45

Hong Kong Lilli: Hard plastic; 7½in (19cm); all three dolls were purchased by their original owner in boxes marked "Marx"; light skin tone; 1958-60.

Left to right:
1. Brunette with red blouse and skirt; high-heeled feet; painted shoes; molded painted earrings.
2. Blonde ponytail with blue lace dress; high-heeled feet; painted shoes; molded painted earrings.
3. Blonde upswept hair; black short sheath dress; high-heeled feet; painted shoes; molded painted earrings.

    MARKS: All three dolls: "U.S. Pat. 2925684//British Pat. 804566//Made in Hong Kong"
    SEE: *Illustration 259. Sherry Dempsey Collection.*
    PRICE: $35-40

M.C. Doll Company

The registered trademarks, the trademarks and the copyrights appearing in italics within this chapter belong to M.C. Doll Company.

Teenage High-Heel Doll: All unbreakable vinyl; 20in (51cm); sleep eyes; rooted hair; satin dress; available in a variety of different sizes and styles in attractive dresses.

> **SEE:** *Illustration 260. Toys and Novelties*, April 1957.
> **PRICE:** $30-45 (depending on costume)

Illustration 260.

Marx (Louis Marx & Co., Inc.)

The registered trademarks, the trademarks and the copyrights appearing in italics within this chapter belong to Louis Marx & Co., Inc., unless otherwise noted.

Miss Seventeen — a Beauty Queen: Hard plastic; 15in (38cm); jointed at neck, shoulders, hips; black rooted hair in ponytail; high-heeled shoes; heavy black eyebrows; *Barbie®* look-alike; 12 outfits; dressed in black *Miss Seventeen* bathing suit; red cape lined in white satin; red shoes; gold crown; gold trophy; 1961.

> **MARKS:** None on doll; "Miss Seventeen//A Beauty Queen" (box)
> **SEE:** *Illustration 261.*
> **PRICE:** $50-65 (complete with box)
> $45-50 (doll in original outfit alone)

Illustration 261.

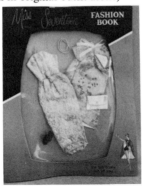

Illustration 262.

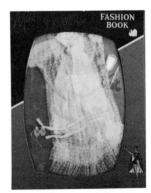

Illustration 263.

Barbie® is a registered trademark of Mattel, Inc.

Miss Seventeen Wardrobe Packaged in a Fashion Book:
1. *On the Town* — white and gold brocade sheath with cap, pearls and red shoes.
2. *Lovely Night* — filmy nylon peignoir; taffeta under slip; comb and mirror; white "mule" type slippers.

Wardrobe created especially for *Miss Seventeen* by the Fashion Institute of Technology by Jay E. Watkins and Edward Roberts.

 SEE: *Illustration 262. Pat Parton Collection.*
 Illustration 263. Pat Parton Collection.
 PRICE: $20-25 (boxed clothing)

Illustration 264.

Illustration 265.

Miss Seventeen Brochure: Wardrobe from left to right:
Top Row
1. *Lovely Night:* cloud soft, white peignoir with matching Grecian-style gown.
2. *American A La Mode:* casual cotton print shirtwaist dress with tiny pearl buttons; net crinoline; white sandals; slim umbrella; handbag; sunglasses.
3. *Rage of Paris:* black faille dress bedecked with a rose; hat and muff of scarlet velvet; rope of pearls; petticoat, panties, black sandals, slim umbrella.
4. *Turnabout:* black wool basic sheath; string of pearls; pink reversible cape; matching velvet bag and hat; pearl necklace, panties, black sandals.
Center Row
5. *On the Town:* gold lamé strapless sheath; satin brocade evening cape; satin clutch bag; long pearl necklace; red sandals.
6. *Wedding Belles:* gown of white taffeta with lace trail; net veil; floral crown; white bouquet; blue garter; pearl necklace; white sandals; petticoat; panties.
7. *Wedding Belles Bridesmaid:* pink embroidered bouffant dress; picture hat to match; net petticoat; bouquet of multi-colored flowers; panties, white sandals.
8. *Champaign Waltz:* yellow transparent nylon gown tied with giant butterly bow; taffeta underskirt with white appliqued flowers; long rope of pearls; panties; sandals.
Bottom Row
9. *Beach Bait:* beauty queen bathing suit; red and white cotton cover skirt; cartwheel sun hat to match; terry towel; carryall bag; sunglasses; red sandals.
10. *Matinee:* theatre two-piece dress; red velvet muff; flowered hat; long pearl necklace; panties.
11. *Date at the Plaza:* three-piece luxury costume; front belted purple velvet coat;

pencil-slim skirt to match; gold blouse (lining of coat in same material); hat and matching muff; black sandals; panties.

12. *St. Moritz:* ski outfit; hooded white ski jacket; red turtleneck sweater; slim black pants; ski boots, mittens; ski poles; sunglasses.

SEE: *Illustration 264.*

Doll House Family: Hard plastic head, hands, feet; cloth over armature body; *Father* 5½in (14cm); *Mother* 5in (13cm); *Boy* 3¼in (9cm); *Girl* 3in (8cm); *Baby* 2in (5.1cm); painted eyes with molded hair; similar to Ideal's *Petite Princess Family®* (see *Illustration 243*); *Father* has beige coat, black pants, red shirt; *Boy* has blue pants with red striped shirt; *Mother* has yellow blouse and black skirt; *Girl* has red dress; *Baby* is wrapped in a blanket; came in a beautiful box with figures of dolls on it; circa 1964.

MARKS: "Marx" (box); none on doll

SEE: *Illustration 265. Dorothy Hesner Collection.*

PRICE: $35-50 (set)

Mattel, Inc.

The registered trademarks, the trademarks and the copyrights appearing in italics within this chapter belong to Mattel, Inc.

Barbie #1:

Barbie's face and body were chic, adult, exotic and beautiful. In spite of opposition from a startled society, *Barbie* caught the imagination of the world and a new era of dolls began.

Barbie was introduced at the New York Toy Fair in 1959. This started a massive Mattel advertising campaign which captured the hearts of little girls. To promote their new teenage doll among retailers, Mattel advertised heavily in the March 1959 issue of *Playthings*, a publication devoted to the doll and toy trade. Their advertisement called *Barbie*, "A Shapely Teen-Age Fashion Model!"

They also printed the pictures of the first extra outfits which are now eagerly sought by collectors. Eventually, the manufacturing of *Barbie* clothes would become one of the largest clothing industries in the world.

SEE: *Illustration 266.*

PRICE: $1500-2000 (mint-in-box #1 *Barbie*)

$ 800-1000 (mint-out-of-box #1 *Barbie*)

Illustration 266.

Petite Princess Family® is a registered trademark of the Ideal Toy Corp.

Barbie #1 in Gay Parisienne Outfit: Solid rigid vinyl torso that has now turned a pale ivory or white; soft vinyl head; 11½in (29cm); jointed at neck, shoulders, hips; blonde or brunette with ponytail and curly bangs; eyes have white irises with very pointed eyebrows; heavy black eyeliner; lips and nails bright red or red orange; holes in both feet that fit into a stand with metal prongs; originally came boxed with black and white striped swimsuit, sunglasses, shoes, gold hoop earrings; fashion booklet; stand not original; 1959.

    MARKS: "Barbie T.M.//PATS PEND.//© MCMLVIII//BY//MATTEL//
    INC." (body)

    SEE: *Illustration 267* (face). *Eleanor Quednau Collection.*
           Illustration 268 (doll). *Eleanor Quednau Collection.*
           Illustration 269 (feet). *Eleanor Quednau Collection.*

    PRICE: $800 (mint-in-package *Gay Parisienne* - outfit only)
           $350-400 (mint-out-of-package *Gay Parisienne* - outfit only)

Illustration 267.   *Illustration 268.*   *Illustration 269.*

Barbie 1959: The following clothes were advertised in the March 1959 issue of *Playthings.* From left to right:

First row

1. *Fashion Undergarments*; 2. *Floral Petticoat*; 3. *Sweet Dreams* (baby doll pajamas); 4. *Apple Print Sheath* (dress); 5. *Cruise Stripes* (camisole top and cotton skirt); 6. *Golden Girl* (gold brocade dress).

Second row

1. *Peachy Fleecy Coat*; 2. *Resort Set* (sailcoat jacket and shorts and striped T-shirt); 3. *Picnic Set* (checked shirt and clam digger pants); 4. *Suburban Shopper* (cotton and lace dress and accessories); 5. *Nighty Negligee Set*; 6. *Sweater Girl* (cardigan sweater set including knitting book and needles).

Third row

1. *Winter Holiday* (fake leather hooded car coat, shirt, zippered knit pants); 2. *Evening Splendour* (golden brocade coat with "mink" cuffs and hat, golden grocade dress); 3. *Gay Parisienne* (strapless dress with "ermine" stole); 4. *Plantation Belle* (shear lace dress with hat); 5. *Easter Parade* (zippered cotton dress, matching hat, taffeta coat); 6. *Roman Holiday* (coat, dress and hat).

To enhance the lovely fashion clothes, Mattel included tiny beautiful accessories and shoes.

Three of these 1959 outfits were made for only one year and are very valuable. They are *Gay Parisienne, Roman Holiday* and *Easter Parade.*

SEE: *Illustration 270. Playthings,* March 1959.

PRICE: $800 (mint-in-package *Gay Parisienne*)
$350-400 (mint-out-of-package *Gay Parisienne*)
$800 (mint-in-package *Roman Holiday*)
$450-500 (mint-out-of-package *Roman Holiday*)
$800 (mint-in-package *Easter Parade*)
$350-400 (mint-out-of-package *Easter Parade*)

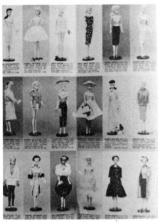

Illustration 271.

Illustration 270.

Barbie #2 (left) and #3 (right):
#2. Solid torso with heavy plastic that has now turned pale ivory or white; same characteristics as #1 except no holes in feet; 11½in (29cm); 1959.
#3. Solid torso with a heavy plastic that has now turned to a pale ivory or white; blonde or brunette ponytail with curly bangs; eyes have blue irises with new curved eyebrows; blue or brown eye shadow; bright red lips (some red-orange); red nails; no holes in feet; came originally in black and white striped swimsuit; sunglasses; shoes; earrings; 11½in (29cm); 1960.

MARKS: "BARBIE T.M.//PATS. PEND.//© MCMLVIII//BY//MATTEL// INC." (body) for both #2 and #3 *Barbie*

SEE: *Illustration 271. Sandy Goss Collection.*

PRICE: $1500-2000 (mint-in-box #2 *Barbie*)
$ 800-1000 (mint-out-of-box #2 *Barbie*)
$ 250-350 (mint-in-box #3 *Barbie*)
$ 150-200 (mint-out-of-box #3 *Barbie*)

Barbie 1960: This advertisement shows additional clothes added to the *Barbie* line in 1960. *Barbie* is shown wearing *Solo in the Spotlight,* a black glitter evening gown. Other outfits pictured from left to right are:
1. *Silken Flame*
2. *Busy Gal*
3. *Friday Nite Date*

4. *Enchanted Evening*
5. *Let's Dance*
   SEE: *Illustration 272. Playthings*, March 1960.
   PRICE: Outfits only (mint-in-package):
   $110-125 (*Solo in the Spotlight*)
   $ 55 (*Silken Flame*)
   $115 (*Busy Girl*)
   $ 90 (*Enchanted Evening*)
   $ 55 (*Let's Dance*)

Illustration 272.

Illustration 273.

Barbie and Ken 1961: Advertisement in *Playthings*, March 1961. *Ken* (*Barbie's* boyfriend) was introduced with his own wardrobe. *Barbie* had new hairdo styles, new hair colors, new costume sets. Tuxedo outfit shown next to *Ken* in striped bathing suit. *Ken's* wardrobe from left to right:
Top row
1. *In Training* (shorts, T-shirt, weights); 2. *Bedtime*; 3. *Casuals*; 4. *Dreamboat*.
Bottom row
1. *Sports Shorts*; 2. *Terry Togs*; 3. *Campus Hero*; 4. *Saturday Date*.
Barbie's advertised new wardrobe from left to right:
Top row
1. *American Airlines Stewardess*; 2. *Open Road* (striped slacks, colored top; car coat with hood); 3. *Ballerina* (leotard and tutu); 4. *Registered Nurse*.
Bottom row
1. *Sheath Sensation*; 2. *Singing in the Shower*; 3. *Orange Blossoms*.
   SEE: *Illustration 273.*

From left to right *Barbie* #2, *Barbie* #4, *Lilli*
Barbie#2: For general characteristics, see *Illustration 271.*
Barbie #4: Began to use a new plastic that remained a tan tone which did not fade to a whitish tone of the earlier *Barbies*; solid torso; blonde or brunette ponytail with curly bangs; eyes have blue irises with curved brows; bright red lips and nails (some red orange); came with black and white striped swimsuit, sunglasses, shoes, earrings; 11½in (29cm); face same as #3 *Barbie*; 1960.
Lilli: For general characteristics, see *Illustration 250.*

MARKS: "BARBIE T.M.//
PAT'S. PEND.//MCMLVIII
//BY//MATTEL//INC."
(body)
SEE: *Illustration 274. Sandy Goss
Collection.*
PRICE: $1500-2000 (mint-in-box
#2 *Barbie*)
   $ 800-1000 (mint-out-
      of-box #2 *Barbie*)
   $ 200-225 (mint-in-box
      #4 *Barbie*)
   $ 125-175 (mint-out-of-
      box #4 *Barbie*)

Illustration 274.

Illustration 275.

Barbie #5: New hollow torso which
keeps its tan tone (a few still sold with
solid body); harder plastic arms; blue
eye shadow and blue irises on eyes;
curved brows; face the same as #3 and
#4 *Barbie*; various hair colors; soft or
firm textures on ponytails and curly
bangs; new "bubble cut" hair style;
bright red lips and nails (some lips a
red-orange); swimsuits came in several
different colors; new wrist tags; no
sunglasses; 1961.
   MARKS: "BARBIE®//PATS.
   PEND//MCMLVIII//BY//
   MATTEL//INC." (body)
   SEE: *Illustration 275. Sandy Goss
   Collection.*
   PRICE: $100-125 (mint-in-box #5
   Barbie)
      $ 75-90 (mint-out-of-
      box #5 *Barbie*)

Barbie Bodies from left to right:
1. New hollow torso which keeps its
   tan tone; first used in 1961.
2. Solid torso; heavy plastic used on
   Barbies #1, 2, 3, 4. The body on the
   #4 *Barbie*, while solid, does not
   turn pale ivory or white but keeps
   its tan tone.
A few *Barbies* with the ® marking have
been seen with solid bodies.
   SEE: *Illustration 276. Sandy Goss
   Collection.*

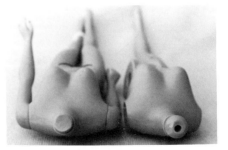

Illustration 276.

Ken: #1 model; rigid vinyl; 12in (31cm); blonde or brunette hair in a crew cut style; the first *Ken,* 1961, had flocked hair that gradually wore away; the following year *Ken's* hair was changed to a molded painted hairstyle; jointed at neck, shoulders, legs; blue painted eyes; pink lips; thick painted eyebrows; fingers all molded together; boxed black tuxedo for #1 *Ken*; white shirt, maroon bow tie and cummerbund; black socks and shoes; came with plastic boxed corsage; careful attention paid to details of costume; 1961.

    MARKS: "Ken T.M.//Pats. Pend.//cMCMLX//BY//MATTEL//INC."
       (lower body)
    SEE: *Illustration 277* (close-up of hair).
           Illustration 278 (doll).
    PRICE: $90-120 (mint-in-box)
           $45-70 (mint-out-of-box)
           $55-60 (tuxedo mint-in-package)

Illustration 277.

Illustration 278.

Barbie: Left — #3 *Barbie* with its box; original outfit called *Silken Flame*; red velveteen top with white bouffant satin skirt, gold belt and purse, black shoes; 1960. Right — #5 blonde ponytail *Barbie* with second *Barbie* box; new hollow body; original outfit called *Winter Holiday*; vinyl white jacket, blue striped cotton T-shirt with hood, black stretch pants, plaid zipper bag, red vinyl mittens and white wedgies; 1961 (doll), 1962 box (box is a year later).

    MARKS: See *Illustration 271* (#3) and *Illustration 275* (#5).
    SEE: *Illustration 279.*
    PRICE: $250-350 (mint-in-box #3 *Barbie*)
           $150-200 (mint-out-of-box #3 *Barbie*)
           $ 55 (mint-in-package *Silken Flame*)
           $ 65 (mint-in-package *Winter Holiday*)

Barbie 1962: Advertisement in *Playthings,* March 1962. Mattel again showed the popular *Solo in the Spotlight* outfit. However, *Barbie* was not as heavily advertised as Mattel started to enlarge their line with non-*Barbie* dolls. This year's *Barbie* is the same as #5 *Barbie.* Two changes were made. *Barbie's* bathing suit was changed to a

Illustration 279.

solid red jersey and other lip colors
were added.

SEE: *Illustration 280.*

PRICE: $110-125 (mint-in-pack-
age *Solo in the Spotlight* outfit
only with all accessories including microphone)

Illustration 280.

Illustration 281.

Barbie and Ken: Left (*Barbie*) — rigid
vinyl body; soft vinyl head; 11½in
(29cm); non-bendable legs; hollow
body; platinum blonde hair which has
faded to yellow; pink lips; painted blue
eyes and eye shadow; heavy black eye
liner; original outfit *Ski Queen*; blue
fur-lined hooded parka, light blue
stretch pants, red mittens, boots, plastic
skis and poles; 1963-1964 (doll and
outfit); Right (#1 Ken) — outfit is later
than this #1 *Ken; Ski Champion;* red
quilted jacket, black stretch ski pants
and matching hat, black cloth mittens
and boots; skis and poles; 1963-1964
(outfit).

SEE: *Illustration 282.*

PRICE: $65 (mint-in-package *Ski
Queen* outfit only)

$65 (mint-in-package *Ski
Champion* outfit only)

Barbie, Ken and Midge: Advertised in
Playthings, March 1963. Again the
Barbie line was heavily featured in
Mattel advertising because they had
had a "fantastic" year in 1962. New
was an expansion of the cases which
could be used for all the doll clothes.
Also new were the mold marks on both
Barbie and the newly introduced
Midge, Barbie's friend.

SEE: *Illustration 281. Playthings,*
March 1963.

Illustration 282.

Midge (Barbie's Girlfriend): Slightly taller body with the same characteristics as 1963 *Barbie* except for a different face; blue eyes; freckles, rooted blonde, brunette, titian Saran hair in "flip" hair style; high-heeled feet; came with two-piece swimsuit in various colors; could wear *Barbie* clothes; 1963.

MARKS: "MIDGE T.M.// ©1962//BARBIE®//©1958// BY//MATTEL, INC." (body)
SEE: *Illustration 283.*
PRICE: $90-120 (mint-in-box)
$45-70 (mint-out-of-box)

Illustration 283.

Fashion Queen Barbie: Rigid vinyl body, soft vinyl head; 11½in (29cm); molded brown hair pulled back and held by a blue band; molded hairdo needed to make it easier to put wigs on; painted blue sleep eyes; blue eye shadow; heavy black eye liner; orange-red lips, finger and toenails; hollow body; came with three wigs — brown red and platinum styled in three different ways; gold and white striped bathing suit with matching bandana; high-heeled shoes; fashion booklet; black wire stand; 1963. Shoes and earrings in picture were not in original box.

MARKS: "MIDGE TM// ©1962//BARBIE® ©1958//BY MATTEL, INC.//PATENTED" (lower body)
SEE: *Illustration 284.*
PRICE: $150-200 (mint-in-box)

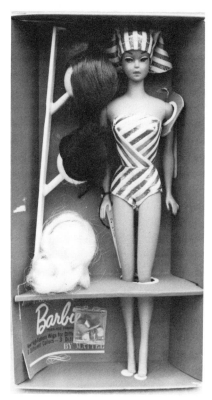

Illustration 284.

Barbie: Rigid vinyl body; soft vinyl head; 11½in (29cm); nonbendable legs; hollow body; painted blue eyes with blue eye shadow; light brown curved eyebrows; red lips, finger and toenails; left doll — dark brown bubble cut hair; original dress *Evening Splendor*, gold metallic brocade coat with real fur cuffs, matching strapless sheath, real fur cap trimmed with pearls, brown shoes; dress dates from 1960-1963; right doll — blonde ponytail with curly bangs; dress is *Enchanted Evening*, pink satin formal gown, real white fur stole, pearl necklace and earrings, sparkling heels; 1959-1964 (dress); 1963-1964 (dolls).

MARKS: "MIDGE T.M.// ©1962//BARBIE®//©1958// BY//MATTEL, INC.//PAT-ENTED."

SEE: *Illustration 285.*

PRICE: Outfits only (mint-in-package):

$65 (*Evening Splendor*)
$90 (*Enchanted Evening*)

Illustration 285.

Molded Hair Ken: Hard plastic hollow torso; 12in (31cm); jointed at neck, shoulders; hips; new blonde or brunette molded and painted crew cut hair; 1962.

Doll at left: 1962 *Ken*; (Not original *Ken* clothes.)

Doll at right; new type of hard plastic with hollow torso; 11¾in (30cm); kneecaps have a different sculpture; arms slightly shorter and fatter; stands easier than older *Ken*; wears tennis outfit with matching jacket; 1963.

MARKS: 1962 doll: "Ken T.M.// PATS. PEND.//CMCMLX// BY//MATTEL//INC."(body)
1963 doll: "Ken®// ©1960//by//Mattel, Inc.//Hawthorn// Calif., U.S.A." (body)

SEE: *Illustration 286. Sandy Goss Collection.*

PRICE: $80-100 (mint-in-box)
$35-60 (mint-out-of-box)

Illustration 286.

Illustration 287.

Barbie and Ken: Left (#1 Ken) — original outfit is later than this *Ken*; *Dr. Ken*; white doctor's jacket and pants, white shoes and socks, package came with surgeon's mask and cap, black bag, stethoscope and reflector head band; 1963 (outfit); Right (*Barbie*); original outfit *Registered Nurse*; white cotton uniform with matching hat, blue cape lined in red, black glasses and white shoes; accessories include hot water bottle, diploma, medicine bottle and metal spoon; 1963 (doll); 1961-1964.

SEE: *Illustration 287.*
PRICE: (outfits only mint-in-package):
$75 (*Nurse*)
$65 (*Doctor*)

Barbie: Original outfit *Barbie Baby Sits;* pink striped apron with black lettering; vinyl baby dressed in a white flannel diaper with extra diaper; kimono-type sacque which is white with pink polka dots; baby came in pink bassinette with lining; pink cotton pillow; flannel blanket; many other accessories included school books, brass clock, black glasses, white phone; single page phone book, list, nursing bottle, bottle of pop, box of pretzels; 1963.

SEE: *Illustration 288.*
PRICE: $95-110 (outfit only mint-in-package)

Illustration 288.

Barbie and Friends: Advertisement in *Playthings*, March 1964. The advertisement read, "The most sensational Barbie Doll ever! Her knees actually bend...her eyes actually open and close." They called her *Miss Barbie*. *Barbie* and *Ken* were pictured in their Hawaiian travel costumes. *Skipper* and *Allan* were introduced and *Midge* was continued.

SEE: *Illustration 289.*

Illustration 289.

Swirl Ponytail Barbie: Vinyl; 11½in (29cm); hollow torso that keeps its tan tone; eyes have blue irises and curved eyebrows; various lip colors; hair has all-firm texture; red swimsuit; bangs pulled back over to one side; 1964.

MARKS: "Midge TM//©1962 //Barbie®//c1958//by// Mattel, Inc.//Patented" (body)

SEE: *Illustration 290. Sandy Goss Collection.*

PRICE: $200 (mint-in-box)
$100-150 (mint-out-of-box)

Illustration 290.

Illustration 291.

Barbie and Ken: Left - Original outfit *American Airlines Stewardess*, blue flight suit with matching hat and bag, white body blouse, black shoulder purse, silver wings; 1963-1964; Right - Boxed outfit dates later than #1 *Ken; American Airlines Captain;* blue suit with silver insignia, matching cap, flight log and bag; shoes and socks; 1961 (*Ken*); 1964 (outfit).

SEE: *Illustration 292.*

PRICE: Outfits only (mint-in-package):
$55-65 (*Stewardess*)
$55-65 (*Pilot*)

Miss Barbie: Life-like bendable knees; eyes that open and close; molded head with orange band; three wigs in various shades of blonde, brunette, titian with three different styles; came with a wig stand; dressed in a one-piece pink swimsuit and matching bathing cap; high-heeled shoes; booklet; lawn swing and planter included; gold colored wire stand; wearing *Sophisticated Lady;* tiara missing; 1964.

MARKS: "5" on left rear; "©1958//MATTEL, INC.// U.S. PATENTED//U.S. PAT. PEND." (right rear); "© M.I." (back of neck)

SEE: *Illustration 291. Eleanor Quednau Collection.*

PRICE: $400-475 (mint-in-box with all accessories, furniture, etc.)

Illustration 292.

Barbie & Ken Little Theatre Brochure: Mattel introduced a new line of theatre costumes that could be used on their own theatre stage. The stage came with drop curtains, backdrops, scenery, scripts, tickets, chair, throne, bed table that could be folded into a carrying case. Mattel also made a series of costumes for *Barbie* and *Ken* that could be used on the stage. These include *Cinderella, Prince, Red Riding Hood and the Wolf, King Arthur, Guinevere, Barbie Arabian Nights* and *Ken Arabian Nights.* Each costume came with a leaflet with the story and illustrations; 1964. (Brochure dated 1963.)

SEE: *Illustration 293.*

PRICE: Outfits only (mint-in-package):
  $ 75-100 (*Cinderella*)
  $ 65-85 (*Prince*)
  $125-150 (*Red Riding Hood and Wolf*)
  $ 75-100 (*King Arthur*)
  $ 75-100 (*Guinevere*)
  $ 70-80 (*Barbie Arabian Nights*)
  $ 60-75 (*Ken Arabian Nights*)

Illustration 293.

Illustration 294.

Ken: Hard plastic hollow torso; 12in (31cm); molded hair; jointed at neck, shoulders, and hips; original outfit from *Barbie's* Theatre line; *Ken* is costumed as *The Prince* from "Cinderella;" green velvet and gold brocade outfit; gold velvet cap with feather and jewel; slippers; tights; ruff; glass slipper on velvet pillow; 1964 outfit.
  SEE: *Illustration 294. Evelyn Smith Collection.*

Skipper (*Barbie's* Little Sister): Vinyl plastic; 9¼in (24cm); jointed at neck shoulders, hips; headband on long straight hair with bangs; hair came in blonde, brunette, titian; wears one-piece red and white playsuit; red shoes; comb, brush, black wire stand in box; had own wardrobe which could be purchased. 1964.
  MARKS: "Skipper//©1963// MATTEL, INC." (body)
  SEE: *Illustration 295. Evelyn Smith Collection.*
  PRICE: $60-70 (mint-in-box)
      $25-30 (mint-out-of-box)

Illustration 295.

"Junior-Edition" styles for Skipper, Barbie's Little Sister: This is an early *Skipper* fashion brochure. *Skipper's* fashions are coordinated with *Barbie* and sometimes *Ken* fashions.

Top (left to right): 1. *DREAMTIME* #1909. Comes dreamtime, *Skipper* wears dainty ruffle-trimmed pink polka-dotted pajamas with pink "flannel" peignoir and pink scruffs. She has a cuddly toy kitten, a telephone and a telephone book. Matches up with *Barbie's Nighty-Negligee.* 2. *SKATING FUN* #1908. *Skipper* cuts a cute figure in her skating costume — red tights topped with attached white turtleneck sweater, red velvet circular skirt lined with calico, furry muff and cap, white figure skates. Matches up with *Barbie's Icebreaker.*

Bottom (left to right): 1. *BALLET LESSONS* #1905. Everything for rehearsal and the big recital. *Skipper* has practice leotard and tights plus a pink lamé-and-net tutu, flower headdress, ballet shoes in carrying bag and a program. Matches up with *Barbie's Ballerina.* 2. *MASQUERADE PARTY* #1903. *Skipper's* masquerade costume is a junior edition of *Barbie's:* yellow and black with glitter-net ruching, matching clown hat, black panties, black shoes with yellow pompons, black mask. She has her own invitation, too. Matches up with *Barbie's* and *Ken's Masquerade.* 1964. (Brochure dated 1963.)

SEE: *Illustration 296.*
PRICE: $15-40 (mint-in-package outfits for *Skipper*)

Illustration 296.

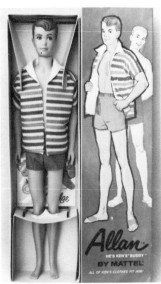

Illustration 297.

Allan: Same body as 1964 *Ken;* molded red hair and brown eyes; dressed in blue bathing trunks; multi-colored striped jacket; blue and tan sandals; booklet and stand; wears the same wardrobe as *Ken,* 1964.

MARKS: "©1960//by//Mattel, Inc.//Hawthorn//Calif., U.S.A." (body)
SEE: *Illustration 297. Sandy Goss Collection.*
PRICE: $65-75 (mint-in-box)
$35-45 (mint-out-of-box)

Skooter: (*Skipper's* Friend); vinyl; 9¼in (24cm); brown eyes; hair has two side ponytails; straight legs; dressed in two-piece red and white swimsuit; comb; brush; booklet; stand; 1965.

MARKS: "©1963//Mattel, Inc." (body)

SEE: *Illustration 298. Sandy Goss Collection.*

PRICE: $60-70 (mint-in-box)
$35-45 (mint-out-of-box)

Illustration 298.

Ricky: (*Skipper's* Friend); vinyl; 9¼in (24cm); painted red hair; straight legs; blue shorts; multi-colored striped jacket; sandals; booklet, stand; 1965.

MARKS: "©1963//Mattel, Inc." (body)

SEE: *Illustration 299. Sandy Goss Collection.*

PRICE: $65-75 (mint-in-box)
$35-50 (mint-out-of-box)

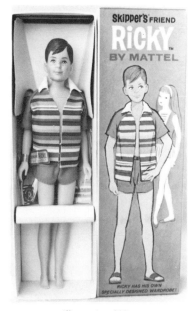

Illustration 299.

Barbie with "American Girl" or so-called "Dutch Boy Style"; new bend-able knees; four hair colors; one-piece cotton swimsuit with multi-colored striped top and solid teal bottom; 1965.

MARKS: "©1958//Mattel Inc.// U.S. Patented//U.S. Pat. Pend." (body)

SEE: *Illustration 300. Sandy Goss Collection.*

PRICE: $200-250 (mint-in-box)
$ 95-115 (mint-out-of-box)

Illustration 300.

Color Magic Doll and Costume Set: 11½in (29cm) bendable legs; long straight hair in either golden blonde or midnight brunette; one-piece diamond pattern swimsuit and headband; hair and costume colors could be changed with application of solution which came with set; instructions told how to style hair; hair changed from midnight to ruby red; golden blonde changed to scarlet flame; solution changed the green diamond in the swimsuit to purple and the yellow to red. Doll was introduced in a booklet dated 1965; however, it was actually a 1966 doll.

The costume gift set also includes pink slacks with patterned trim, skirt and blouse of the same pink, blue and white print. These clothes also changed color with the solution.

Today *Barbie* gift sets are rare and eagerly sought by collectors.

MARKS: "C1958 Mattel, Inc.//U.S. Patented// U.S. Pat. Pend.//Made in Japan" (body)

SEE: *Illustration 301. Susan Miller Collection.*

PRICE: $250-350 (mint-in-box blonde hair *Barbie*)
$400-600 (mint-in-box brunette hair *Barbie*)

Illustration 301.

Unusual Barbies Wearing "Fashion Queen" Swimsuit: Left — doll has "swirl" ponytail; right — doll has "bubble cut" hairdo; dolls never removed from box.

SEE: *Illustration 302. Gayle Elam Collection.*

PRICE: $250 (brunette Swirl *Barbie* mint-in-box)
$125 (blonde Ponytail *Barbie* mint-in-box)

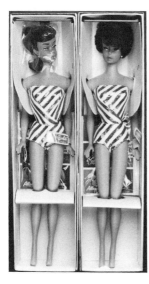

Illustration 302.

Illustration 303.

Chatty Cathy: (doll on right) rigid vinyl body with soft vinyl face; 20in (51cm); sleep eyes; open-mouth with two teeth protruding; no open grill on stomach but cloth covers some form of grillwork; rooted short brunette hair; brown sleep eyes with lashes; jointed at neck, shoulders, hips; $\vee$ on back side; freckles over nose; all original; blue cotton dress with embossed flowers and lace trim; pink velvet slippers with bow; string in back of neck which operates voice; 1960. This doll has an excellent quality vinyl and voice mechanism. It still operates clearly and distinctly.

    MARKS: "Chatty Cathy T.M.//Patents Pending//cMCMLX//BY MATTEL, INC. HAWTHORNE, CALIF." (in box on lower back); "MATTEL, INC.// M//TOYMAKERS" (in circle directly below square).

    SEE: *Illustration 303.*

    PRICE: $55-60

Chatty Cathy: (doll on left) same general characteristics as doll on right. However, this doll is a later model and the vinyl, while still rigid, is not of the same quality. The stomach has an open grill not covered with cloth; blonde rooted hair; blue sleep eyes with lashes; clothes all original except shoes; blue cotton jumper-type dress with white neck and sleeves; dress tagged "Chatty Cathy//by//Mattel"; 1962.

    MARKS: "CHATTY CATHY T.M.//PATENTS PENDING//CMCMLX// BY MATTEL INC.//HAWTHORNE, CALIF" (in middle of back).

    SEE: *Illustration 303.*

    PRICE: $50-55

New Chatty Cathy: (doll in middle) same vinyl body as 1962 doll; very different hard vinyl face which by now often turns sticky; brunette rooted hair; blue sleep eyes with real lashes; head placed differently on body; all original dress which is similar to *Charmin' Chatty*; red velvet top with white skirt; red ribbon sash; shoes not original; says 18 phrases when the "magic ring" is pulled; 1963.

    MARKS: "CHATTY CATHY R//©1960//CHATTY BABY T.M.//©1961//BY MATTEL, INC.//U.S. PATENT 3,017,187//OTHER U.S. &//FOREIGN

PATS. PEND.//PAT. IN CANADA 1962" (in middle of back)
SEE: *Illustration 303.*
PRICE: $45-55

Notes: *Chatty Cathy* dolls with brown eyes are rarer than those with blue eyes and command higher prices. Very few voice boxes are still operating; dolls which are still "talking" cost more. Collectors should be aware that the mechanism is very delicate and will not last indefinitely. The doll, itself, is an excellent quality doll.

Chatty Cathy: Introduced in March 1960, *Chatty Cathy* was the second big hit for Mattel. She was 20in (51cm) tall and could say 11 different things at random by pulling a "magic ring" near her neck.
Phrases are:

1. What do we do now?
2. Give me a kiss.
3. Let's play school.
4. I'm so tired.
5. Please brush my hair.
6. Will you play with me?
7. I love you.
8. Do you love me?
9. Change my dress.
10. May I have a cookie?
11. Let's have a party.

Advertised on Mattel's "Matty's Funday Funnies" which they claimed was the highest rated network program on daytime TV.
MARKS: "CHATTY CATHY T.M. PATENTS PENDING//cMXMLX//BY MATTEL, INC.//HAWTHORNE, CALIF." (in box on lower back) "MATTEL//M//TOYMAKERS" (in circle directly below square)
SEE: *Illustration 304. Toys and Novelties*, March 1960.

Illustration 304.

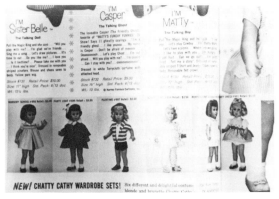

Illustration 305.

Chatty Cathy Wardrobe Sets: Introduced at Toy Fair in New York in February 1961. From left to right:

1. Nursery school dress.
2. Party coat.
3. Playtime outfit.
4. Sleepy Time.
5. Peppermint Stick dress.
6. Party dress.

SEE: *Illustration 305. Toys and Novelties,* March 1961.

Chatty Cathy: In 1962 *Chatty Cathy* was still going strong and Mattel introduced her baby sister, *Chatty Baby. Chatty Cathy* still says 11 phrases.

MARKS: "CHATTY CATHY T.M.//PATENTS PENDING //cMCMLX//BY MATTEL, INC.//HAWTHORNE, CALIF." (in the middle of the back)

SEE: *Illustration 306. Playthings,* March 1962.

Illustration 306.

Illustration 307.

New Chatty Cathy: "Now she says 18 different things at random-and is more appealing than ever in her brand-new party dress and double pony tail hairdo! You can comb her hair into a page boy once her hair ribbons are removed." 1963.

This doll has a different look as can be seen in *Illustration 303* center.

MARKS: "CHATTY CATHY R//c1960//CHATTY BABY T.M.//c1961//BY MATTEL, INC.//U.S. PATENT 3,017,187//OTHER U.S. & FOREIGN PATS. PEND// PAT IN CANADA 1962" (in the middle of the back)

SEE: *Illustration 307. Playthings,* March 1963.

PRICE: $45-55

Chatty Cathy Patterns: Original advertising stand for dress patterns for the "Original talking doll by Mattel"; eight fashion designs with easy to follow Advance patterns; 1962.

Pattern Group G: Coat and hat; rickrack dress; pajamas; robe.

Pattern Group F: Pleated skirt and blouse; sports set; dress; nightgown.

Fabrics illustrated feature Eastman Chromspun and Estron acetate.

SEE: *Illustration 308.*

PRICE: $5 each pattern.

Illustration 308.

Illustration 309.

Charmin' Chatty: Introduced at the New York Toy Fair in 1963, *Charmin' Chatty*, a straight-haired ordinary little girl wears glasses. She was advertised as the first doll that really plays with you and says 120 different things. She operates with a record mechanism operated by a pull string. The records can be changed. Her "play" wardrobe included clothes, accessories and records.

The different sets were:

1. *Let's Play Cinderella*
2. *Let's Play Together*
3. *Let's Play Nurse*
4. *Let's Go Shopping*
5. *Let's Play Tea Party*
6. *Let's Talk 'N Travel In Foreign Lands*

She also had game sets with records to play alone with her or up to four players. These include:

1. *Chatty Animal Friends* and *Chatty Animal Round-up*
2. *Chatty at the Fair* and *Chatty Skate 'n Slide*

SEE: *Illustration 309. Playthings*, March 1963.

PRICE: $50-60

Charmin' Chatty as Cinderella: boxed outfit came in a *Let's Play Cinderella* kit which included ball gown, patchwork dress, plastic slippers which gave the illusion of glass; record with 24 different phrases pertaining to the story.

SEE: *Illustration 310. Pat Parton Collection.*

PRICE: $20-25 (outfit)

Illustration 310.

Illustration 311.

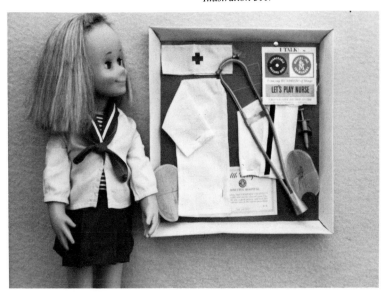

Charmin' Chatty Let's Play Nurse: Back of package "You're the nurse...Charmin' Chatty's the patient. Here is everything you both need including a Chatty Record. She really plays along with you...she'll say 24 new and different things...just the right thing...and you can take care of her.//You can tell it's Mattel...it's swell!" Glasses are missing; bangs have been cut; 1963.

MARKS: "CHARMIN' CHATTY TM//c1961 MATTEL INC.// HAWTHORNE, CALIF. USA//U.S. PAT. 3,017,187//PAT'D IN CANADA 1962//OTHER U.S. & FOREIGN//PATENTS PENDING"

SEE: *Illustration 311.*

PRICE: $20-25 (outfit)

Mayfair of Canada

The registered trademarks, the trademarks and the copyrights appearing in italics within this chapter belong to Mayfair of Canada.

DOLLS NOT PHOTOGRAPHED

Debbie: Vinyl with soft vinyl head; 10½in (27cm); jointed at neck, shoulders, waist, hips; high-heeled; came wiht booklet "Around the World with Debbie//Mayfair's Teen-Age Doll."

MARKS: "P" in circle

Model Toys Ltd.

The registered trademarks, the trademarks and the copyrights appearing in italics within this chapter belong to Model Toys Ltd.

DOLLS NOT PHOTOGRAPHED

Teenage Doll: Plastic body with soft vinyl head; 9in (23cm); high-heeled; long blonde hair; circa 1965.

MARKS: "Model Toys Ltd//Hong Kong" (back)

M.G.M. Sales, Inc.

The registered trademarks, the trademarks and the copyrights appearing in italics within this chapter belong to M.G.M. Sales, Inc.

Illustration 311A.

Illustration 312.

Mollye Goldman was a well-known designer of children's clothes and her clothes were beautiful. She was very active during the high fashion period designing for Eegee and other companies. She did put out lines of dolls from time to time and her *Perky* dolls were marketed by the M.G.M. Sales, Inc., of Upper Darby, Pennsylvania.

SEE: *Illustration 311A. Playthings,* March 1962.

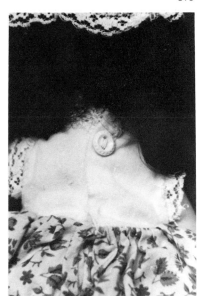

Illustration 313.   *Illustration 314.*

Perky as a Colonial Girl: Hollow plastic body and legs; vinyl arms; soft vinyl head; 9in (23cm); rooted hair; sleep eyes with molded eyelashes; closed-mouth; Y on back side; 2nd and 3rd fingers molded together and slightly curved; jointed at neck, shoulders, legs; dress with cotton pink, blue and tan print skirt; blue top with white and gold braid; white cotton pantaloons and slip; second net slip; velvet shoes with gold ornament; Mollye button; all original clothes; circa early 1960s.

    MARKS: "Mollye" (back of head); no tag on clothes

    SEE: *Illustration 312.*

    PRICE: $20-30 (depending on costume)

Perky: Same general characteristics as *Illustration 312;* Alice in Wonderland-type costume; blue rayon dress with lace trim; white cotton apron trimmed with embroidered flowers; white slip attached to dress; velvet shoes with gold ornament; clothes all original; Alice-type long blonde hair; circa early 1960s.

    Perky came in many different costumes. Mollye designed clothes for many of the doll companies of the period.

    MARKS: "Mollye" (back of the head); "created//by//Mollye" (tag sewn into panties)

    SEE: *Illustration 313. Pat Parton Collection.*

    PRICE: $20-30 (depending on costume)

Perky: Button on *Perky* clothes.

    MARKS: Sometimes the clothes are labeled. Sometimes they are not.

    SEE: *Illustration 314.*

Nancy Ann Storybook Dolls, Inc.

The registered trademarks, the trademarks and the copyrights appearing in italics within this chapter belong to Nancy Ann Storybook Dolls, Inc.

This California company made the very popular *Nancy Ann Storybook Dolls* first in bisque and then in hard plastic. *Muffie*, an 8in (20cm) hard plastic walking doll, was added to the line in 1953.

When the high-heeled dolls became popular, a beautiful vinyl 10½in (27cm) fashion doll called *Miss Nancy Ann* and a smaller high-heeled 8in (20cm) doll were added to their line. Both had a large selection of clothes which could be purchased separately. These outfits followed the high fashion trends of the end of the 1950s and were beautifully made. In March 1959 the Nancy Ann Company advertised matching clothes for both the *Muffie* and the *Miss Nancy Ann*.

The company also made dolls called *Debbie* and *Lori Ann*. (See *Hard Plastic Dolls,* pages 191 and 192), and they advertised all of them except *Debbie* in 1961. After this, production problems multiplied for the company when Nancy Ann Abbott became ill. She died in 1964, and they ceased producing dolls.

In the highly competitive fashion field of the late 1950s and early 1960s, the dolls and clothes designed by Miss Abbott are outstanding. They are highly prized by today's collectors.

Illustration 315.

Illustration 316.

Muffie: All vinyl; 8in (21cm); walking doll; sleep eyes; rooted hair; 1957.
SEE: *Illustration 315. Toys and Novelties*, January 1957.
PRICE: Not enough samples available.

Miss Nancy Ann: Rigid vinyl body; soft vinyl head and arms; 10½in (27cm); blue sleep eyes with molded lashes; rooted long thick dark auburn hair that could be curled and combed; painted red lips, toe and fingernails; jointed at neck, shoulders, hips; rouged cheeks; pearl earrings; high-heeled; original tagged outfit; red corduroy trimmed with white lace, fur hat and muff; circa 1958-1959.
MARKS: "NANCY ANN" faint lettering (head)
SEE: *Illustration 316.*
PRICE: $50-60

Illustration 317.   *Illustration 318.*

Miss Nancy Ann: Left — original outfit; blue with white polka dots skirt and blouse trimmed with white lace; red vinyl belt and purse; blue felt hat with red netting; nylons; white shoes; Right — red, yellow and brown plaid flannel skirt; red jersey top; red purse; black shoes; both dresses tagged, "Styled by Nancy Ann/Nancy Ann Storybook Dolls, Inc./San Francisco, California"; circa 1959.
MARKS: "NANCY ANN" (head)
SEE: *Illustration 317.*
PRICE: $50-60

Miss Nancy Ann: Left — blue and brown cotton "Egyptian" print skirt and jacket trimmed with gold braid and white lace; sheer white blouse; white straw hat trimmed with white net and gold braid; blue purse; Right — red and white striped cotton skirt and blouse; red straw hat with white ribbon; white and red braid trim; red purse; circa 1959.
MARKS: "NANCY ANN" (head)
SEE: *Illustration 318.*
PRICE: $50-60

Miss Nancy Ann: Left — blue denim with red print; red and white striped blouse; red vinyl belt; black shoes; Right — brown skirt with white polka dots; white sheer blouse trimmed with white lace; circa 1958.

    MARKS: "Nancy Ann" (head)

    SEE: *Illustration 319.*

    PRICE: $50-60

Miss Nancy Ann (smaller version) Rigid vinyl body, soft vinyl head and arms; 8in (20cm); blue sleep eyes with molded lashes; high heeled; jointed at neck, shoulder, legs; red lips. Left — blonde hair; turquoise corduroy skirt trimmed with yarn; turquoise jersey bodice trimmed with silver; matching tights and hat trimmed with white yarn; silver skates; original clothes. Right — brown rooted hair; riding clothes; beige corduroy jodhpur; black riding jacket; white scarf; black plastic riding hat; white boots; circa 1959.

    MARKS: None on doll; ice skater tagged "Styled by Nancy Ann" (inside skirt)

    SEE: *Illustration 320.*

    PRICE: $45-55

Illustration 319.

Illustration 320.

Nasco (See also Kaysam)

The registered trademarks, the trademarks and the copyrights appearing in italics within this chapter belong to Nasco Inc., unless otherwise noted.

Hello, Dolly Doll: Plastic body, vinyl head and arms; 21in (53cm); sleep eyes with real lashes; eye shadow above the eyes; curly blonde rooted hair; jointed neck, shoulders, hips; high heeled; red taffeta dress with inset red taffeta with silver glitter; white gloves; 1961.

This is not a portrait doll but gives the general impression of Carol Channing in her famous Broadway role.

This is a Kaysam marked doll.
MARKS: "K//19©61" (head)
SEE: *Illustration 321.*
PRICE: $95-105

Illustration 321.

Carol Channing: Plastic vinyl, soft vinyl arms and head; 11½in (28cm); *Barbie®* look-alike; side-glancing eyes with heavy black eye liner; blonde rooted hair; orange lips; high arched eyebrows; all four fingers molded together with separate thumb; dressed in red taffeta dress; inset front red panel trimmed with red fringe and glitter; black velvet choker necklace with rhinestones; high-heeled feet; circa 1961.

This doll is attributed to Nasco. Dolls with the same description and marking are also attributed to New Dolly Toy Co. Both companies are known to have marketed dolls with AE markings.
MARKS: "AE" (head)
SEE: *Illustration 322.*
PRICE: $25-30

Barbie® is a registered trademark of Mattel, Inc.

Illustration 322.

Natural Doll Co., Inc.

The registered trademarks, the trademarks and the copyrights appearing in italics within this chapter belong to Natural Doll Co., Inc.

The Natural Doll Co., Inc., marked its 50th anniversary in 1965. They celebrated at the 1965 Toy Fair in New York by introducing an anniversary doll and placing an advertisement in the March 1965 *Playthings*. Along with a picture of the new doll, they showed lovely drawings of their earlier dolls dressed in the styles of each decade. From top to bottom right they were the dolls of 1915, 1925, 1935, 1945, 1955 and 1965. The company produced a variety of dolls including babies, toddlers, girls and teenagers. They used different materials over the years.

> **SEE:** *Illustration 323. Playthings*, March 1965.

Illustration 323.

Illustration 324.

Miss Anniversary: Vinyl; 24in (61cm); walking mechanism; rooted hair; packaged in anniversary box; 1965.

> **MARKS:** "Miss Anniversary// It's a Natural Walking Doll" (box)
> **SEE:** *Illustration 324. Playthings*, March 1965.
> **PRICE:** $40-50

Doll in Fur Coat: High-heeled fashion
doll; 14R type; 1959.
SEE: *Illustration 325. Toys and
Novelties,* June 1959.
PRICE: $35-45

Illustration 325.

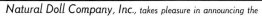

Advertisement for Angela Cartwright Doll: Published in *Toys and Novelties* in March 1961; shows both 14in (36cm) and 30in (76cm) dolls.
See also General Foods, page 111.
    SEE: *Illustration 326.*
    PRICE: $100-125

Angela Cartwright Doll: Hollow rigid vinyl body with softer but firm head; 20in (51cm); molded open-mouth with four painted teeth; brownish-gold sleep eyes with lashes; feathered (three unequal lines) eyebrows; individual fingers; jointed at neck, shoulders, hips; dressed in blue-faded-to-purple taffeta dress with a white nylon apron printed with pink lines and red hearts; red hair bow on rooted hair ponytail; walking mechanism; instructions say, "Just take me by the left hand-walk me slowly, first on one foot and then the other. TO SIT ME DOWN - pull my legs UP into sitting position. BEFORE taking me for another walk, push my legs back until you hear them CLICK." All original; 1961.
    MARKS: "Angela" (neck)
    SEE: *Illustration 327.*
    PRICE: $100-125

Illustration 327.

Illustration 328.

Illustration 329.

Illustration 330.

Box for Angela Cartwright doll: Large pink box with pictures of Angela demonstrating how to play with the doll. It says, "You can change my pretty clothes — made especially for me." The front of the box has a picture of Danny Thomas and says, "Angela Cartwright Doll//Featured as Linda Williams//Starlet of the Danny Thomas TV Show."
   SEE: *Illustration 328.*

Miss Puff: Party doll; blows up a balloon; blows up a party favor; blows her bubble pipe.
   SEE: *Illustration 329. Playthings,* June 1964.

Doll in Braids: The Natural Doll Co. Inc. advertised in *Playthings,* March 1963 that they were "Famous for Beautiful Braids."
   SEE: *Illustration 330.*

DOLLS NOT PHOTOGRAPHED
Miss Ritzi: Vinyl with soft vinyl head; 17in (43cm); rooted hair; sleep eyes; jointed at neck, shoulders, waist, hips; tyical 14R face; see pages 103-104; circa 1959.
   MARKS: "A//14R" (head); "B-18" (back)
This doll also was made in a 10½in (27cm) version. She had a swivel waist.
   MARKS: "Circle X" or "Circle P"

P

Ⓟ is not a company name but rather the mark and head mold of dolls made during the late 1950s and into the very early 1960s.

The 10½in (27cm) high-heeled fashion doll was very popular, and the major doll companies used them in quantity. Marketing companies bought either parts or whole dolls and assembled and/or dressed them for resale. The Ⓟ head mold was popular with these sales companies, and it is often impossible to identify them unless they are found in the box or with a known outfit. Companies producing the more expensive dolls sometimes used this same head mold, but their face painting, rooted hair, and body were of a superior quality.

The companies marketing the less expensive dolls used coarse rooted hair that did not wash and curl well. Often the bodies were made of inferior vinyl or plastic. The design and quality of their "fashion" clothes, while often attractive, were of poor workmanship. Less accessories were available.

Ⓟ dolls were usually marked in two ways. The first was a horizontal line that may have been a plate inside the mold with a Ⓟ underneath. See *Illustration 331*. The second marking is the same horizontal plate line but without the Ⓟ . See *Illustration 332*.

Examples of known companies that used Ⓟ dolls include Admiration, Arranbee, Beehler Arts, Belle, Sayco, Uneeda and Princess Anna. Often these and other companies had Ⓟ dolls with several different prices within their own line. The same parent comany may have had several satellite companies with different Ⓟ lines.

There are at least two Ⓟ dolls that do not follow the general pattern of other Ⓟ dolls. They are the *Miss Coty®* doll by Arranbee, see page 72, and the *Princess Anne®* doll by Princess Anna Doll Co., Inc., see page 189. The heads have both marked and unmarked Ⓟ molds. Their rooted hair is long and thick so that it can easily be washed and styled. The bodies are similar to the *Miss Revlon®* dolls. The Arranbee clothes are excellent and expensive while the Princess Anna dolls' clothes are less expensive.

Miss Coty® is one type of Ⓟ doll that is easy to identify because of the high quality, but many other Ⓟ dolls pose identification problems.

SEE: *Illustration 331* (Ⓟ mark).
Illustration 332 (Ⓟ mark).
PRICES: This will vary greatly according to the quality of the doll. However, it is a joy to find a high quality Ⓟ doll.

Coty® is a registered trademark of Coty Div. Pfizer.
Princess Anne® is a registered trademark of the Princess Anna Doll Co., Inc.
Revlon® is a registered trademark of Revlon, Inc.

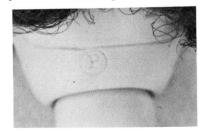

Illustration 331.

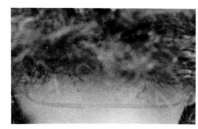

Illustration 332.

Illustration 333.   *Illustration 334.*

(P) **High-Heeled Dolls:** 10½in (27cm); examples of different ways the faces were painted; faces especially vary in the way eyelashes were painted on the eyes; some (P) dolls do not have any painted eyelashes; quality of the hair varies from doll to doll; circa 1959.

Although each doll's hair is different, all five have a coarse-type hair.

MARKS: " (P) " and horizontal plate line on back of head; or only line on head.
SEE: *Illustration 333.*
Illustration 334.
PRICE: $15-30

Illustration 335.

Sally Starr: Rigid vinyl body; soft vinyl arms, head; 10½in (27cm); sleep eyes with molded lashes; three painted eyelashes at side of eyes; thick rooted blonde hair in a ponytail; jointed at neck, shoulders, no joints at hips; high-heeled; white felt cowboy outfit with red and blue trim; red boots; white felt cowboy hat; red nail polish; Sally Starr was a TV personality on Philadelphia Channel 6 "Popeye Theatre" from 1950 to 1972; dolls were dressed in several types of these wagon wheel cowboy costumes; circa late 1950s.

MARKS: "(P) " (back of neck); "U"(body near waist); (possibly a Uneeda body)
SEE: *Illustration 335.*
PRICE: $45-55

P & M Doll Company Inc.

The registered trademarks, the trademarks and the copyrights appearing in italics within this chapter belong to P & M Doll Company Inc.

Illustration 336.

Illustration 337.

Paula Mae: Vinyl; high-heeled dolls from 12in (31cm) to 26in (66cm).
  SEE: *Illustration 336. Toys and Novelties,* February 1957.

Paula Mae: Vinyl plastic; 18in (46cm); open-closed mouth with molded tongue; sleep eyes with real eyelashes; dimples over individual fingers; red rooted hair; unusually soft vinyl head and body which feels almost like "Magic Skin" dolls; tag says that it will not crack, chip or peal and is completely sanitary; yellow dress and bonnet with black trim; circa 1963. This doll was advertised in *Playthings,* March 1963.
  MARKS: "15" (head); tag reads, "*P & M Paula Mae//I'm washable from head to toe; Look! My hair can be washed, combed, curled.*"
  SEE: *Illustration 337. Pat Timmons Collection.*
  PRICE: $50-60

Plastic Molded Arts

Glamour Doll: All-vinyl; 20in (51cm); rooted hair; jointed at neck, shoulders, waist, hips; high heeled; 1957.
Top doll in advertisement
Miss Joan: Hard plastic with soft vinyl head; 12in (31cm); rooted hair; jointed at neck, shoulders, hips, knees; high heeled; lace panties, bra; fashioned stockings; 1957.
Doll on right in advertisement
Little Miss Joan: Hard plastic with soft vinyl head; 9in (23cm); high-heeled walker; came with wardrobe; Saran hair; 1957 (doll on left in advertisement). Plastic Molded Arts advertised in 1957 that they were playing "Sugar Daddy" to their dolls by providing them with real mink stoles.
SEE: *Illustration 338. Toys and Novelties*, March 1957.

Illustration 338.

Illustration 339.

Girl in Leotard: Hollow plastic body and legs, rigid non-poseable vinyl arms, soft vinyl head; 10½in (25cm); sleep eyes with molded lashes; four lines at corners of each outer eye; typical PMA face; red rooted hair; jointed at neck, arms, legs; high-heeled shoes; wears black leotard with large red vinyl belt, red shoes; circa 1959-60.
Both dolls have the same body. They were made for the mass market and could be purchased inexpensively.
MARKS: "PMA" (head)
SEE: *Illustration 339.*
PRICE: $10 each

Palitoy Company

The registered trademarks, the trademarks and the copyrights appearing in italics within this chapter belong to Palitoy Company, unless otherwise noted.

DOLLS NOT PHOTOGRAPHED

Child dolls: This company was very active from 1957 to 1965. They made many child dolls with beautiful clothing. These dolls usually carry the mark of "Palitoy" on the body or head.

Tressy: Vinyl; 12in (31cm); varied hair colors; grow hair mechanism which uses push button and a key; turquoise painted eyes; many outfits and accessories could be purchased for this doll; 1964-1965 and reintroduced in 1979. She had a 9in (23cm) sister named *Toots* with same grow hair mechanism. She also had a wardrobe and accessories.

Mary Make-up: This doll was the same size and type as *Tressy*® and could wear her clothes. She came with a pale complexion and platinium blonde hair. She was the high-heeled fashion type. Included with the doll were cosmetics called "application sticks." Her hair could also be colored.

Pedigree of England

The registered trademarks, the trademarks and the copyrights appearing in italics within this chapter belong to Pedigree Company, unless otherwise noted.

DOLLS NOT PHOTOGRAPHED

The children in England had dolls like those in the United States but they were made by English companies. In 1962 Pedigree made a *Sindy* doll which is still popular. She has always competed with *Barbie*®, and her wardrobe has kept up with the latest fashion.

Sindy: Vinyl; 12in (31cm); jointed at neck, shoulders, hips; painted face with blue side-glancing eyes; thick short "bouncy" rooted hair; came with "weekenders" which included bell-bottom jeans with matching red, white and blue jersey top; red hair band; white tie shoes; 1962.

By 1966 she followed *Barbie*® and had bendable arms and legs. She was called *"Sindy-the Model."*

Petitcollin

The registered trademarks, the trademarks and the copyrights appearing in italics within this chapter belong to Petitcollin.

Doll from France — Marie Ange: Vinyl; 20in (51cm); wide eyes that have a flirty glance; sleep eyes fringed with thick lashes; jointed at neck, shoulders, hips; rooted blonde hair; basic outfit includes socks and shoes; clothes could be ordered; dresses are Paris-designed; upswept hairdo created by noted French hair stylist; pictured dress is white dotted cotton; bow trims on each sleeve and skirt; Sears catalog; circa 1963.

Playthings magazine of February 1963 carried a similar advertisement saying "*nouveau visage de la poupee modern,* imported from France."

    SEE: *Illustration 340. Sears catalog,* see page 245.
    PRICE: $35-45

Tressy® is a registered trademark of the American Character Doll Co.   *Barbie*® is a registered trademark of Mattel, Inc.

Princess Anna Doll Co., Inc.

The registered trademarks, the trademarks and the copyrights appearing in italics within this chapter belong to Princess Anna Doll Co., Inc., unless otherwise noted.

Princess Anne: Rigid vinyl body and soft vinyl head; 10½in (27cm); high heeled; jointed at neck, shoulders, hips, waist; head uses ℗ mold; (see page 184); rooted hair; body similar to *Little Miss Revlon®* doll; blue sleep eyes; high curved brown eyebrows; three brown eyelashes at outer edges of eyes; painted red lips, fingernails, toenails; rooted thick long white hair; pearl earrings; blue party dress with velvet bodice and satin skirt; silver rickrack trim; gripper snap with "Rau Sklikits" packed in plastic "see through" box; circa 1958.

The body of this doll has the same quality as the Arranbee *Miss Coty®* doll. However, the clothes are inferior.

MARKS: ℗ (head)
SEE: *Illustration 340A.*
PRICE: $25 (in box)

Illustration 340A.

Reliable Doll Company of Canada

DOLLS NOT PHOTOGRAPHED
Teenage Doll: Plastic with soft vinyl head; 11½in (29cm); *Barbie®* look-alike; painted eyes with heavy eye liner; molded lashes; circa early 1960s.
MARKS: "Reliable//Canada"

Revlon® is a registered trademark of Revlon, Inc.
Coty® is a registered trademark of Coty Div. Pfizer.

Remco Industries

The registered trademarks, the trademarks and the copyrights appearing in italics within this chapter belong to Remco Industries.

Littlechap Family Brochure: Hard vinyl body, soft vinyl head and arms; rooted hair; molded painted face; fingers molded together; 1963. From the brochure "Meet the Littlechap Family."

"*Mr. John Littlechap, Lisa,* his wife, and their two daughters...17 year old *Judy* and 10 year old *Libby.* Never before has a family of dolls been created that is so true-to-life."

Dr. John Littlechap: 15in (38cm); "Father of the *Littlechap Family*...member of the Lanesville County Medical Society former Flight Surgeon U.S. Army Air Force...loves his family and golf...wishes he could find more time for both."

Lisa Littlechap: 15in (38cm); "Mother of the *Littlechap Family*...attractive Mother of *Judy* and *Libby* former model, wonderful cook...president of the P.T.A. and the best dressed woman in town."

Judy Littlechap: 13½in (34cm); "Big sister of the *Littlechap Family*...age seventeen, honor student at Lanesville High School senior class...loves parties and crazy desserts."

Libby Littlechap: 10½in (27cm); "Kid sister of the *Littlechap Family*...age 10, fifth grader at Lanesville Elementary School...loves to climb trees, pester her sister and wants to be a doctor like her Daddy."

Illustration 341.

Illustration 342.

MARKS: Each doll has the name in a circle above other marks//"Littlechap//
Remco Industries//c1963" (center back).

PRICE: $40-45 *John Littlechap*
$40-45 *Lisa Littlechap*
$30-35 *Judy Littlechap*
$30-35 *Libby Littlechap*

SEE: *Illustration 341* (Brochure Cover).
Barbara Andresen Collection.
Illustration 342 (Brochure).
Illustration 343 (Brochure).
Illustration 344 (Brochure).

Illustration 345 (Brochure).
Illustration 346 (Brochure).
Illustration 347 (Brochure).
Illustration 348 (Brochure).
Illustration 349 (Brochure).

LIBBY'S PLAID REEFER COAT

Style #1303/Price $2.98

LISA'S FUR TRIMMED SUEDE COAT

Style #1204/Price $3.98

DR. JOHN'S ALL WEATHER COAT

Style #1411/Price $3.50

JUDY'S RED CHESTERFIELD COAT

Style #1103/Price $3.98

Illustration 343.

Illustration 344.

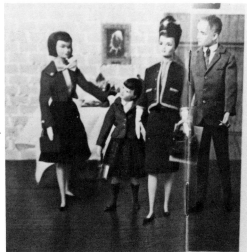

JUDY'S THREE-PIECE SUIT

Style #1102/Price $3.50

LIBBY'S THREE-PIECE BLAZER OUTFIT

Style #1302/Price $3.50

LISA'S THREE-PIECE CHANEL SUIT

Style #1202/Price $3.75

DR. JOHN'S BUSINESS SUIT

Style #1410/Price $4.50

LISA'S FORMAL EVENING ENSEMBLE
Sweeping full length coat of blue satin, lined in silver and blue patterned brocade. Standaway portrait neckline, deep cuffs of white ermine-like fur, long slim blue satin evening skirt with fishtail hemline, fitted overblouse with scoop neckline and slim straps of blue and silver brocade.
ACCESSORIES: Silver slippers, silver clutch bag, drop earrings, hair ornament, beautiful necklace, opera length white nylon gloves.
(Doll not included)
Style #1205/Price $4.98

DR. JOHN'S TUXEDO
Black dress suit, satin lapels and dress trousers with satin stripe. White sheer shirt with pleated front and pearl studs.
ACCESSORIES: Black bowtie, black satin pleated cummerbund, black socks and black shoes, black wallet and white carnation.
(Doll not included)
Style #1412/Price $4.98

Illustration 345.

JUDY'S BATHING ENSEMBLE
Orange, blue, green and yellow striped terry cloth poncho with attached hood. Hood lining and binding in bright orange. Two-piece orange stretch bathing suit with orange and white braid trim.
ACCESSORIES: Straw hat with orange and blue ribbons, matching straw tote with orange and blue trim, orange frame sunglasses and white beach shoes.
(Doll not included)
Style #1105/Price $2.98

JUDY'S NIGHTSHIRT
Pink and orange striped cotton man-tailored shortie nightshirt, pearl buttoned with roll up sleeves.
ACCESSORIES: Orange fuzzy mules, fuzzy white stuffed poodle.
(Doll not included)
Style #1107/Price $1.50

JUDY'S FOOTBALL OUTFIT
Beige corduroy car coat with attached hood, patch pockets and gold buttons, lined in red, yellow and black tartan plaid, matching plaid tapered slacks, black bulky knit, V-neck pu
ACCESSORIES: Matching p
red leatherette mittens, g
chrysanthemum, black boo
pennant, gold chain with g
(Doll not included)
Style #1105/Price $4.75

JUDY'S DANCE DRESS
Two-piece ensemble with yellow taffeta, sleeveless, scooped neckline dance dress, belted in dainty floral embroidered French ribbon, matching yellow velveteen

LIBBY'S LINGERIE
White tricot lace-trimmed panties, lace-trimmed white cotton slip with petticoat bottom of pleated nylon
short   Pink puppy
(Doll not included)
Style #1304/Price $1.75

JUDY'S LINGERIE
Pink lace bra, pink tricot half-slip with lace trim and matching pink lace trimmed panties, nylon stockings.
(Doll not included)
Style #1108/Price $1.75

LISA'S LINGERIE
Black lace bra, black tricot half-slip with lace trim and matching black lace trimmed panties, nylon stockings.
(Doll not included)
Style #1206/Price $1.75

Illustration 346.

Illustration 347.

Remco Industries
Harrison, New Jersey

DR. JOHN'S PAJAMAS

Blue and white striped classic two-piece pajamas. ACCESSORIES: Tortoise shell eyeglasses, slippers, medical journal. (Doll not included)
Style #1414
Price $2.25

LISA'S PEIGNOIR AND NIGHTGOWN ENSEMBLE

Red crepe bias-cut short nightgown with bodice of red lace. Matching red lace peignoir with huge puffed sleeves and crepe tie for standaway portrait neckline. ACCESSORIES: Red mules, long stemmed rose, hand mirror. (Doll not included)
Style #1201
Price $3.50

LIBBY'S PAJAMAS

Two-piece pajamas with three-quarter-length pants of yellow print. French smock top of bright blue with matching print lining, bell-shaped sleeves. ACCESSORIES: Red mules, diary, stuffed toy. (Doll not included)
Style #1301
Price $1.98

JUDY'S PAJAMAS

Tailored two-piece pajamas with solid orange slacks. White striped top trimmed with orange pockets, cuffs and front band. ACCESSORIES: White mules, comb, brush, mirror, French poodle. (Doll not included)
Style #1106
Price $1.98

Illustration 348.

Illustration 349.

LIBBY'S LEVIS AND SWEATSHIRT

Blue denim Levis with fly front and white stitching, classic white sweatshirt. ACCESSORIES: Red and white sneakers, comic book, and YoYo, white socks. (Doll not included)
Style #1305/Price $2.25

LISA'S WHITE TWO-PIECE DRESS

Completely lined two-piece dress with slim skirt and V-necked, long sleeved overblouse belted in tawny beige suede with gold buckle. ACCESSORIES: Tawny beige printed chiffon scarf, golden tan pumps, golden tan leatherette over-sized tote bag, gold sunburst pin and gold button earrings. beige gloves. (Doll not included)
Style #1203/Price $3.50

DR. JOHN'S GOLF OUTFIT

White wool cardigan sweater, black jersey polo shirt, red twill golf slacks. ACCESSORIES: Plaid cap, two golf clubs, golf balls, and golf trophy, black socks, black shoes. (Doll not included)
Style #1413/Price $3.98

JUDY'S SPORTSWEAR OUTFIT

Box-pleated, knee tickler skirt (made to be worn above knees) in cream, gray, gold and brown houndstooth check, gold suedecloth jerkin, beige shirt with panel front. ACCESSORIES: Deep red, tie-print triangle headscarf, brown loafers, gold knee socks, gold pin, black framed eyeglasses and play script. (Doll not included)
Style #1101/Price $3.75

Rite Lee

The registered trademarks, the trademarks and the copyrights appearing in italics within this chapter belong to Rite Lee.

DOLLS NOT PHOTOGRAPHED
Miss Lynne: Stuffed vinyl; 19in (48cm); rooted hair; sleep eyes; high-heeled fashion doll; earrings; jointed at neck only; circa late 1950s.

MARKS: "14 R" (neck); "Miss//Lynne//Created by Rite Lee" (box)

Roddy of England

The registered trademarks, the trademarks and the copyrights appearing in italics within this chapter belong to Roddy, unless otherwise noted.

DOLLS NOT PHOTOGRAPHED
Beauty Queen: Vinyl; 14in (35cm); blue sleep eyes; rooted Saran hair; jointed at neck shoulders, waist, hips; medium high-heeled feet; dressed in pink swimsuit; "Miss England" sash; pink rose decoration in hair; Alexander *Cissy*® look-alike; circa 1958.

Rosebud

The registered trademarks, the trademarks and the copyrights appearing in italics within this chapter belong to Rosebud.

Scotch Girl in Kilts: Very soft vinyl body and head; 10½in (27cm); short curly rooted hair; glassy decal-type eyes; closed-mouth; dressed in Stuart plaid kilt; black velvet jacket trimmed with lace; black plastic "Cinderella" shoes; plaid socks; late 1950s. The box has a lovely rose printed on the top. *Rosebud* was taken over by Mattel in 1967.

> **MARKS:** "Rosebud" (in script on head); "A Rosebud Doll" (box)
> **SEE:** *Illustration 350.*
> **PRICE:** $35-40

DOLLS NOT PHOTOGRAPHED
Rosette: Plastic body; vinyl arms and head; 14in (36cm); rooted white hair; blue eye shadow; high-heeled feet; circa 1958.

> **MARKS:** "Rosebud" in a key shaped figure with a rose.

Illustration 350.

Cissy® is a registered trademark of the Alexander Doll Co.

Ross Products, Inc.

Illustration 351.

Illustration 352.

Their most famous product was *Tina Cassini* with a wardrobe by Oleg Cassini. They also made the highly collectible *Yogi Berra.*

Tina Cassini: Vinyl; 12in (31cm); *Barbie*®-type; blonde and brunette rooted bubble cut hair; individual fingers; unusually long neck; mold lines on both sides of well-shaped legs; introduced in 1964; listed in Sears catalog in 1965.

This high fashion doll is named for Tina Cassini who is the daughter of Gene Tierney and Oleg Cassini. She has many outfits which could be purchased separately.

> **MARKS:** "Tina Cassini//Made in British//Hong Kong" (back); "Tina Cassini" tag on some but not all clothing
> **SEE:** *Illustration 351* wearing an original yellow mini suit with green felt cloth 'style hat and purse; printed turtleneck blouse; green medium heel shoes; listed in Sears catalog in 1965.
> *Illustration 352* wearing an original white tennis dress with black and white machine embroidery trim around bottom of skirt; plastic tennis racket.
> **PRICE:** $35-50

Barbie® is a registered trademark of Mattel, Inc.

Illustration 353.

Illustration 354.

Illustration 355.

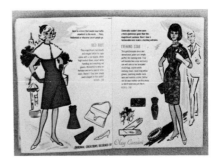

Illustration 356.

The brochure is presented in the format of a fashion show. Each costume is described as it would be if the model were coming down the runway. One interesting comment was, "Did you know that Oleg Cassini is a fabulous skier? And now after skiing at St. Moritz in Switzerland and all the famous slopes in Europe, he has designed the perfect ski outfit for you and Tina."

Tina Cassini: brochure, "Little Lady of Fashion" from left to right:

Illustration 353. Finale for Fashion Show; front cover
Illustration 354. Welcome to Fashion Show; The Dine-N-Dancer
Illustration 355. Green-N-Gay; Glitter Gal
Illustration 356. Red Riot; Evening Star
Illustration 357. Pink Prize; Rain-Stopper
Illustration 358. The Travel Time; The Tina Church Set
Illustration 359. Dots for Day; The Smart Sport
Illustration 360. Sport Shift; Jumper Joy
Illustration 361. The Sea Queen; Tina-for-Tennis
Illustration 362. Sign of Summer; Surf Sensation
Illustration 363. Sweet Dreamer; The Ski Bunny
Illustration 364. Miss Outdoor Gal; Wardrobe List

Illustration 357.

Illustration 358.

Illustration 359.

Illustration 360.

Illustration 361.

Illustration 362.

Illustration 363.

Illustration 364.

Royal Doll Co.

The registered trademarks, the trademarks and the copyrights appearing in italics within this chapter belong to Royal Doll Co., unless otherwise noted.

Joy in a Raincoat: Rigid vinyl body and soft vinyl head; 12in (31cm); rooted hair; large painted brown eyes with blue eye shadow above black eyelashes; closed-mouth; jointed at neck, shoulders, hips; 3rd and 4th fingers molded together; Y on backside; designed by Miss Rose of the Royal Doll Co.; orange dress and panties; white plastic raincoat, hat and umbrella; clothes all original; 1965.

> **MARKS:** "A Royal Doll//19c65"
> **SEE:** *Illustration 365.*
> **PRICE:** $30-35 (depending on costume)

Illustration 365.

Joy as a Bride: Same general characteristics as *Illustration 365;* original white taffeta strapless bride dress; net overdress; trimmed in lace; veil and shoes not original; 1965.

> **MARKS:** "A Royal Doll// 19©65" (head)
> **SEE:** *Illustration 366. Pat Parton Collection.*
> **PRICE:** $30-35 (depending on costume)

Illustration 366.

Joy in France: Same general characteristics as *Illustration 365;* original clothes; white cotton pantaloons trimmed in lace; white cotton petticoat trimmed in lace; dress has blue piqué skirt; white embossed cotton top; white cotton apron with attached shawl-type collar trimmed in blue and turquoise braid; matching mob cap; red hair; 1965.

    MARKS: "A Royal Doll//19c65" (head)

    SEE: *Illustration 367. Pat Parton Collection.*

    PRICE: $30-35 (depending on costume)

Illustration 367.

Illustration 368.

Robin: Plastic body and soft vinyl head; 21in (53cm); long dark brown rooted hair; wearing white nylon dress with red velvet vest; matching red velvet hat; 1965.

    MARKS: "Royal Doll//Robin" (wrist tag); "1965//Royal Doll //9" (head)

    SEE: *Illustration 368.*

    PRICE: $35-45

Lonely Lisa was created by Miss Rose of Royal Doll. She designed for her husband, Henry Frankel, of Royal Doll Company. In 1964 Miss Rose took the doll to visit stores in most major cities to find out how little girls would react to a doll that was neither a baby nor a sophisticated teenager with a mature figure. She said, "Girls — not just little girls either — always reached out for Lisa. They want to pat and comfort her."

Miss Rose took the idea to an Italian sculptor who had never worked with dolls before. The final doll not only had the "lonely" look, but the vinyl part of the arms and legs had a type of wire inside that allowed the doll to clasp her hands, fold her arms, kneel, and so forth.

Lonely Lisa: Soft vinyl head, legs, arms; body and upper arms and legs are cloth; 20in (51cm); painted brown eyes and face; rooted hair; blue and black plaid reproduced dress with white inset at neck; 1964.

> **MARKS:** "19c64//Royal Doll"
> **SEE:** *Illustration 369. Laura May Brown Collection.* (See page 201.)
> **PRICE:** $30-40

Illustration 369.

DOLLS NOT PHOTOGRAPHED

Girl: Hard plastic with vinyl head; 21½in (55cm); flirty blue sleep eyes; jointed at neck, shoulders, waist, hips; 1960.

> **MARKS:** "A ROYAL DOLL 1960" (head); "Royal Doll" (body)

Lady: Hard plastic with vinyl head; 24in (61cm); rooted platinum hair; flirty blue sleep eyes; closed-mouth; jointed at neck, shoulders, waist, hips; 1960.

> **MARKS:** "Royal Doll" (head); "A Royal Doll 19c60" (body)

Sayco Doll Company

Sayco dolls were popular with children for their bright cheerful appeal. They usually were well played with. During the 1950s and 1960s they were often found in mail order catalogs and in department stores' Christmas catalogs.

wardrobe for the *Miss America* line was innovative and followed the fashions current at the time. Today they are scarce and not often found in mint condition.

Illustration 371.

Illustration 370.

Miss America Doll: Rigid vinyl and soft vinyl head; 18in (46cm); jointed at neck, shoulders, hips; high heeled; sleep eyes; 14R-type face; reddish blonde rooted hair; wearing red velvet cape, white brocade dress; circa 1957-59.

MARKS: None on doll; "Miss America//Doll//by Sayco" (box)
SEE: *Illustration 370. Lisa Patrick Collection.*
PRICE: $55-70

Miss America Pageant Doll: Rigid vinyl body and limbs; soft vinyl head; 10in (25cm); high heeled; doll authorized by the Miss America Pageant held in Atlantic City; dark blonde rooted hair; blue sleep eyes with molded eyelashes; jointed at neck, shoulders, waist, hips; 3rd and 4th fingers molded together; original clothes; white and blue cotton bodice with blue skirt; white pearl earrings; a blue ribbon marked "Miss America"; red, white and blue box; circa 1959.

MARKS: "ⓟ" (head); none on body
SEE: *Illustration 371.*
PRICE: $35-45

Illustration 372.

Miss America Pageant Doll — Wave: Hard plastic body and soft vinyl face; 10¾in (27cm) (brochure says 11in [28cm]); rooted hair; excellent flesh color with rosy cheeks; unusually long eyebrows; sleep eyes with molded lashes; no painted eyelashes under the eyes; flat but beautiful face; small gap between neck and head; jointed at shoulders, neck, hips, knees; armhooks (see Identification Guide, *Hard Plastic Dolls*, page 268U); individual fingers; dimples above fingers but not toes; chubby-type doll; navy blue original uniform which has faded to purple; metal stars on collar; red chevron on sleeve; white hat may not be original; leather pocketbook with "U.S.A." on it; doll came with many outfits which could be bought separately; 1959.

    MARKS: Small "s" (head)
    SEE: *Illustration 372.*
    PRICE: $50-70 (including box and brochure)
                $20-30 (outfits)

Miss America Pageant Doll: For general characteristics, see *Illustration 372.*
From left to right:
Banner doll: Original doll came with panties, shoes, socks; banner inscribed "Miss America."
TWA Hostess doll: Light blue-gray uniform and hat; uniform with "TWA" lettering on jacket; silver wings fastened to the cap with ribbons; black purse and shoes; dress was purchased in a box marked, "Miss America Pageant Doll."

    MARKS: "Sayco" (head of brunette doll); small "s" (head of blonde doll)
    SEE: *Illustration 373.*
    PRICE: $35-45 (doll in original outfit)

Illustration 373.

Illustration 374.

Miss America Pageant Doll: For general characteristics, see *Illustration 372.*

From left to right:

Ice Skater doll: Blue skating costume with fur trim; silver skates.

Farmerette: Blue overalls; red and white polka dot blouse and overall trim; straw hat; sandals; ear of corn in pocket.

Both costumes all original and came in boxes which were purchased separately; 1959.

> **MARKS:** Small "s" (head of blonde doll); "Sayco" (head of brunette doll)
> **SEE:** *Illustration 374.*
> **PRICE:** $35-45 (doll in original outfit)

Brochure for Miss America Pageant Doll — description of wardrobe:

Descriptions are for dolls from left to right:

Illustration 375. COVER; Page 3 — letter to new doll owner, "Little Miss America of the Future"; *BACK COVER* — entry blank for a contest with the first prize a trip to the September Miss America Pageant; *Page 14* —

1. Red taffeta formal with silver trim, white rabbit fur stole, sandals.
2. Genuine mink coat and muff.
3. Southern Belle formal, parasol, pantaloons, crinoline, straw hat, slippers.

Illustration 376. Page 2 — description of doll; *Page 15* —

1. Blue cotton coat, white piqué collar and cuffs, red straw hat, pocketbook.
2. Red velvet coat trimmed with white rabbit fur, hat, muff.
3. White rabbit fur coat, hat, muff.
4. Red and blue raincoat with attached hood, boots, umbrella.

Page 4 — explanation for children of the type of girl who can become a Miss America; *Page 13* —

1. Pink bridesmaid dress, straw hat, crinoline, pink slippers.
2. Bridal outfit, pearls, crinoline, slippers.
3. Blue bridesmaid dress, straw hat, crinoline, blue slippers.

Illustration 377. Page 10 —

1. WAC uniform with hat, shoulder strap bag, shoes, socks.
2. WAVE uniform with hat, shoulder strap bag, shoes, socks.
3. TWA hostess outfit.
4. Red satin majorette outfit with blue trim, boots, baton, hat.

Page 7 —

1. White taffeta nurse uniform, red and navy cape, shoulder strap bag, stockings, shoes, cap.
2. Pink and blue knit suit, hat, suede pocketbook, shoes, socks.
3. Farmerette blue overalls, straw hat, red blouse, corn, shoes.
4. School club outfit, brown beanie, shoulder strap bag, brown dress, shoes, socks.

5. Blue denim outfit, orange beanie, turtleneck sweater, brown and white shoes.
Page 12 —
1. Royal blue skating costume, white fur hat, silver skates, blue skating hat.
2. White terry cloth bathing suit and robe, glasses, bathing cap, sandals.
3. Red and white ski suit, skis, red cap, mittens, ski shoes.
4. Jodhpurs, green bowler and turtleneck sweater, riding crop, black boots, belt.
Page 5 — TOP ROW
1. Red and white taffeta dress with lace trim, belt, hair ribbon.
2. Pink ninon dress and slip with lace trim, belt, hair ribbon.
3. Powder blue taffeta dress with lace trim, belt, hair ribbon.
4. Printed picolet multi-colored dress, hair ribbon.
BOTTOM ROW
1. Blue and white polka dot sundress, bonnet.
2. Pink and blue taffeta rosebud pajamas, belt, hair ribbon.
3. Pink and blue taffeta rosebud housecoat, belt, slippers.
4. Two-piece cotton pajamas with embroidery trim.
Illustration 378. Page 8 —
1. Yellow nylon dress, slip, straw hat, pocketbook, shoes, socks, belt.
2. Red taffeta pinafore dress; straw hat, pocketbook, shoes, socks.
3. Pink taffeta dress, white nylon top, straw hat, shoes, socks, pocketbook.

Illustration 375.

Illustration 376.

4. Royal blue and white nylon dress and slip, straw hat, shoes, socks, pocketbook.

Page 9 —

1. Powder blue and white nylon dress and slip, straw hat, shoes, socks, belt, pocketbook.
2. Orchid and white checked cotton dress, straw bonnet, shoes, pocketbook, belt.
3. Pink nylon peignoir, glasses, comb, brush, mirror, pompon slippers, white tulle ballerina outfit with red trim, red slippers, flowers.

Page 6 —

1. Pink embossed cotton bolero dress with blue trim, straw hat, shoes, socks, pocketbook.
2. Aqua cotton suspender dress, blouse, shoes, socks, straw hat, pocketbook.
3. Red Bermuda shorts, cotton shirt, beanie, argyle socks, sandals.
4. Red and white piqué cotton dress, straw hat, shoes, socks, pocketbook.

Page 11 —

1. Red and blue pleated skirt, white or pink leather jacket and hat, shoes, socks, shoulder strap bag.
2. Yellow pleated skirt, twin sweater set and hat, watch fob, shoulder strap bag.
3. Cowgirl outfit, white blouse, red fringed skirt, gold holster, boots, gun, red felt sombrero.
4. Roller skater outfit, blue sweater and hat, red felt skirt with poodle trim, white skates.

Illustration 377.

Illustration 378.

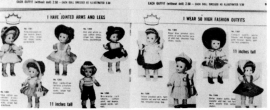

Illustration 379.

Illustration 380.

Teenager in Red Striped Dress, Style #20B: Stuffed vinyl body and head; harder vinyl arms; 19in (48cm); rooted brunette hair; sleep eyes with lashes and three lash lines at corner of each eye; individual fingers; jointed at neck and arms only; red and white striped dress with black ribbon belt and black high-heel shoes; circa 1957-59.

This doll is very different from many other 14R dolls because of the painting of the eyelashes and the wider mouth. It does have the rather flat face of the 14R doll.

    MARKS: "14R" (head); "Sayco//DOLL Corporation//200 Fifth Ave.//New York City" (tag stapled to dress); "Sayco Doll" (on box with blue and yellow flowers)

    SEE: *Illustration 379.* (doll and box)

    PRICE: $25-35

Glamour Girl Bride: Hard plastic body; vinyl head; 23in (58cm); rooted hair; eight eyelashes painted under eyes; molded open-mouth with molded tongue like the Mollye dolls; unusually red cheeks and round face; 3rd and 4th fingers molded together; dressed in "teddy-type" underwear; bride dress has white organdy underskirt with dotted net overskirt with ruffles; net veil with lace trim; circa 1955-1958.

    MARKS: None on doll; "Glamour girl//Sayco Doll" (tag)

    SEE: *Illustration 380. Inga Tomoletz Collection.*

    PRICE: $45-55

Uneeda Doll Co., Inc.

The registered trademarks, the trademarks and the copyrights appearing in italics within this chapter belong to Uneeda Doll Co., Inc., unless otherwise noted.

Uneeda has been a durable doll company. They manufactured dolls before 1920 and their annual line included dolls of various prices and quality. After World War II they quickly adapted to the new hard plastic material and by 1957 they had turned to the popular soft vinyl rooted hair dolls.

They followed the trend toward high-heeled dolls and quickly imitated the Ideal *Revlon*® line with a *Tinyteen* line. Later they produced *Barbie*® look-alikes.

Always interested in character faces and personalities, they made a *Pollyanna* doll in 1960. This represented Hayley Mills who played the part in the Walt Disney movie. The *Blue Fairy* from Walt Disney's *Pinocchio* was featured at the 1962 Toy Fair in New York.

Added to their always interesting line were some of the later *Betsy McCall*® dolls. One was 36in (91cm) tall. This competed well in the oversized doll market.

During this period, Uneeda used a circle gripper snap that looked like ◎ on the outside. The letters "SK Likits Rau" are printed on the inner silver fastener. This is a helpful identification feature. The snap was used on both the small and large dolls.

Illustration 381.

Blue Fairy: Plastic body and legs; vinyl arms and head; 10in (25cm); high heeled; rooted white hair; sleep eyes with molded lashes; dressed as the Blue Fairy from Walt Disney's *Pinocchio*.

    MARKS: "Uneeda" (head)
    SEE: *Illustration 381. Playthings,* March 1962.
    PRICE: $60-70

Revlon® is a registered trademark of Revlon, Inc.
Barbie® is a registered trademark of Mattel, Inc.
Betsy McCall® is a registered trademark of the McCall Corp.

Tinyteen (or Suzette) and Bob: Left (*Bob*) — rigid vinyl body with soft vinyl head 10½in (27cm); brown sleep eyes with molded eyelashes; light brown molded hair; movable arms and legs; white dinner jacket with black pants and tie; circa early 1960s; Right (*Tinyteen*) — rigid vinyl body with soft vinyl head; 10in (25cm); blue sleep eyes with molded lashes; three lashes painted to side of eye; high heeled; jointed at neck, shoulders, waist, hips; rooted long dark blonde hair pulled back in ponytail; blue cotton dress; dress has Uneeda snap; circa 1957-early 1960s.

> **MARKS:** "UNEEDA" (back of both heads); none on body
> **SEE:** *Illustration 382.*
> **PRICE:** $35-45 each (higher for unusual outfit)

Illustration 382.

Illustration 383.

Pollyanna: Soft vinyl head and body; rigid vinyl limbs; 10in (25cm); high heeled; long blonde rooted hair; blue sleep eyes with molded lashes; three lashes to side of eye; closed-mouth with red lips; jointed at neck, shoulders, hips; one-piece body with no swivel waist; 3rd and 4th fingers molded together and slightly curled; original clothes except for red ribbon and bow; red checked dress and pantaloons; white eyelet lace trims both the slip and pantaloons; doll is dressed as the character Pollyanna played by Hayley Mills in the Walt Disney movie; dress has Uneeda snap; 1960.

> **MARKS:** "UNEEDA" (back of head in faint letters)
> **SEE:** *Illustration 384.*
> **PRICE:** $40-50

Tinyteen: Rigid vinyl with soft vinyl head; 10½in (27cm); for general characteristics, see *Illustration 382;* dressed in satin and lace dress and veil; circa 1957-1960.

> **MARKS:** Unknown
> **SEE:** *Illustration 383. Sharlene Doyle Collection.*
> **PRICE:** $45-55 (mint-in-box)

Illustration 384.

Illustration 385.

Girl in Red Dress: Rigid vinyl body with soft vinyl face; 19in (48cm); jointed at neck, shoulders, hips, waist; sleep eyes with real lashes; ten lashes painted below the eyes; blonde rooted hair; high heeled; *Cissy*®-type face; red nylon dress with white rose and ribbon; small white hat with braid of red and white chiffon; all original; earrings; dress has Uneeda snap; circa 1957-1960.

　　MARKS: "Uneeda//2S" (head)
　　SEE: *Illustration 386.*
　　PRICE: $35-45

Illustration 387.

Pollyanna: Light hollow rigid vinyl body and legs; soft vinyl arms and head; 31in (79cm); blonde rooted hair; sleep eyes with lashes; lashes painted under eyes with wedge-shaped paint at outer corner of each eye; open/closed mouth with eight teeth; jointed at neck, shoulders, hips; all original except for hat; red checked dress and pantaloons with eyelet trim; spats over black shoes; doll is dressed as Hayley Mills in the role of Pollyanna in the Walt Disney movie; dress has Uneeda snap; 1960.

　　MARKS: "© WALT DISNEY// PRODS.//MFG BY UNEEDA //5//N.F." (head)
　　SEE: *Illustration 385.*
　　PRICE: $85-100

Illustration 386.

Girl in Green Dress: Rigid vinyl body with soft vinyl head; 19in (48cm); sleep eyes with real lashes; painted lashes under eyes; jointed at neck, shoulders, waist, hips, just above knees; green satin dress with large red rose; matching picture hat with red rose; red shoes; high heeled; all original; circa 1956-1967.

　　MARKS: "Uneeda//2S" (head)
　　SEE: *Illustration 387. Marybeth Manchook Collection.*
　　PRICE: $35-45

Cissy® is a registered trademark of the Alexander Doll Co., Inc.

Betsy McCall®: Plastic body and soft vinyl face; 11½in (29cm); sleep eyes; rooted hair; dressed in white skirt with red trim, navy blue top, red belt; white hat; all original; circa 1959-1961.

The box says, "Betsy McCall//child fashion doll//can be purchased wearing other style combinations of smart wearing apparel as shown below//created exclusively for McCall//by Uneeda Doll Co. Inc. Brooklyn, N.Y."

Other sizes included 22in (56cm), 29in (74cm) and 36in (91cm)

> **MARKS:** None on doll
> **SEE:** *Illustration 389* (doll). *Kathy George Collection.*
> *Illustration 390* (box). *Kathy George Collection.*
> **PRICE:** $70-80 (in box)

Illustration 389.

Illustration 390.

Miss Twist: Hard plastic Dollikins body with 16 flexible joints; soft vinyl head; 19in (48cm); sleep eyes with lashes; rooted fluffed bobbed hair; headband; earrings; satin dress; can duplicate any position in the "twist;" 1962.

> **MARKS:** "Uneeda 2S" (head)
> **SEE:** *Illustration 391. Toys and Novelties,* April 1962.
> **PRICE:** $35-50 (doll in street clothes)
> $50-60 (cocktail dresses, formals, velvet pedal pushers with nylon blouse)
> $70 (unusual outfits)

Illustration 391.

Betsy McCall® is a registered trademark of the McCall Corp.

212

Illustration 392.

***Barbie®** Look-alike:* left to right:
1. Uneeda *Suzette:* 11½in (28cm); see *Illustration 392;* original clothes; circa 1962.
2. Uneeda *Suzette:* 10½in (27cm); see *Illustration 392;* original clothes; blue taffeta evening dress; net over-skirt with silver thread running through; pearl earrings; plain small silver gripper snap; circa 1962.
3. Eegee: 11½in (28cm); not original clothes; circa 1961-1962. 1961-1962.
> **MARKS:** See *Illustration 392.* Eegee doll *Marianne Gardner Collection.*
> **SEE:** *Illustration 393.*
> **PRICE:** $10-15

Illustration 394.

***Barbie®** Look-alikes:* Very different dolls; left to right:
1. Uneeda *Suzette:* 11½in (29cm); narrow eyes with white iris and small pupil; pointed chin; wide mouth; 1962.
2. Uneeda *Suzette:* 10½in (27cm); plastic body and legs; rigid vinyl arms; soft vinyl head; smaller petite U-shaped face; wider eyes than *Suzette* (above); large white pupils; heart-shaped mouth; high-arched eyebrows; swirl ponytail; circa 1961-62.
> **MARKS:** Doll on left: "N.F." (head); "Uneeda Doll Co. 1962" in circle (back); Doll on right: "U" (head)
> **SEE:** *Illustration 392.*
> **PRICE:** $10-15

Illustration 393.

Suzette: Hard plastic upper torso; vinyl legs, arms, head; 11½in (23cm); *Barbie®* look-alike; rooted red hair pulled back into a braid; painted black side-glancing eyes; jointed at neck, shoulders; unusual hips; high-heeled feet that are very tiny; original pink dotted swiss dress with lace trim; very pretty doll with excellent sculpturing; 1962.
The dress has the Uneeda gripper fastener with "SK LIKITS RAU" on the inner silver fastener.
> **MARKS:** "N.F." (head); "©// UNEEDA//DOLL CO.// INC." in circle//."1962" (body)
> **SEE:** *Illustration 394.*
> **PRICE:** $10-15

Barbie® is a registered trademark of Mattel, Inc.

Coquette: Hard Plastic body and legs; hard vinyl arms; soft vinyl head; 16in (41cm); rooted very curly blonde hair with pigtails; character face; large blue sleep eyes with lashes; three-line feathered eyebrows; dimple in chin; light pink lips; individual fingers; dimples in knees; orange, black, white, yellow plaid dress; white eyelet apron; Uneeda closing snap (see page 208.); original clothes; shoes and socks not original; circa 1963.

Illustration 395.

> **MARKS:** "UNEEDA DOLL//
> Co. INC.//©1963" (back)
> **SEE:** *Illustration 395.*
> **PRICE:** \$25-30

Illustration 396.

Vermont Maid®: Plastic with soft vinyl head; 15in (38cm); rooted red hair with braids; green eyes; long graceful fingers; high-heeled feet; jointed at neck, shoulders, hips; green cotton jumper over white blouse; advertising doll for Vermont Maid Syrup; circa 1964.

Uneeda used the "U" marking for many dolls during this period.

> **MARKS:** "U 26" (at rooted hairline); other numbers reported have been "22" and "18"
> **SEE:** *Illustration 396. Laura May Brown Collection.*
> **PRICE:** \$15-25

DOLLS NOT PHOTOGRAPHED

Freckles: Plastic body and legs; vinyl arms and head; 32in (81cm); rooted reddish hair; blue flirty sleep eyes with lashes; open/closed mouth with four molded teeth; 2nd and 3rd fingers on left hand curled; 3rd finger on right hand curled; freckles across nose and cheeks; circa 1960-1961.

> **MARKS:** "22" (body)

Princess Doll: Plastic body and legs; vinyl arms and head; 32in (81cm); rooted pink acetate hair; same doll as *Freckles;* from the Walt Disney movie *Babes in Toyland;* circa 1960-61.

> **MARKS:** "Uneeda/13" (head)

Vermont Maid® is a registered trademark of Nabisco Brands.

Unique Doll Company

High-Heeled Teen: Rigid vinyl body, soft vinyl head; 10½in (27cm); platinum blonde rooted hair that does not wash well; blue sleep eyes; three painted brown eyelashes at side of eyes; red lips, finger and toenails; jointed at neck, shoulders, one-piece body and legs; no swivel waist; clothes appropriate but not original; circa 1959.
  MARKS: "P"(head); "UNIQUE" (body)
  SEE: *Illustration 397.*
  PRICE: $20-30

Illustration 397.

Illustration 398.

Ellie May Clampett: Plastic body and soft vinyl head; 12in (31cm); blonde rooted hair pulled into pigtails; curly bangs; painted side-glancing blue eyes; jointed at neck, shoulders, hips; 2nd, 3rd and 4th fingers molded together; blue and white striped cotton shirt; blue denim pants with white rope belt; tennis shoes; 1964.

This is not a portrait doll but it has an excellent likeness of the character Ellie May played by Donna Douglas in the television show "Beverly Hillbillies." This is the same doll called *Calico Lass* used by Kelloggs for advertising.
  MARKS: "Unique" (head)
  SEE: *Illustration 398.*
  PRICE: $30-35

Unknown

The years of 1957 to 1965 were a particularly difficult period for identification because there were many new marketing techniques used to sell these dolls. Well-known companies sold unmarked dolls through catalog companies and specialty stores. They also set up additional divisions within their own company. (Example Horsman-Couturier.)

Sometimes companies were formed just to promote one or two special dolls. This occasionally happened when a designer wanted to market his own designs. It also happened to promote special dolls sponsored by television programs or popular movies. After the promotion, these companies faded from the scene.

Another marketing technique placed thousands of beautiful dolls in the grocery stores where they could be purchased inexpensively at the checkout counter along with groceries. Occasionally, these dolls were offered as premiums to store shoppers. Many of these were unmarked and their boxes unmarked.

Hopefully, someone will identify these dolls and add to our knowledge.

Girl in Pink Print Dress: Hard plastic body, rigid vinyl legs, soft vinyl head and arms; 15in (38cm); sleep eyes with eyelashes; painted eyelashes under eyes; very red smiling mouth; rooted hair; jointed neck, shoulders, waist, hips; long slender legs; individual fingers; high-heeled feet; nice flesh tone; circa 1957.
MARKS: None
SEE: *Illustration 399. Eryn Judd Collection.*
PRICE: $15-20

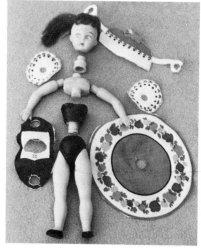

Illustration 399.

Illustration 400.

Mary-Lou — Doll Mannequin: Plastic; 9in (23cm); came with second head and four outfits stamped on cotton; colors coordinated so that more outfits could be made; no directions but when one takes the doll apart, as shown in *Illustration 400*, it is possible to dress the doll without any sewing or gluing; circa early 1960s.

    MARKS: "Japan" (doll); "Mary-Lou" (box)
    SEE: *Illustration 400.*
    PRICE: $25

Cloth Wardrobe for Boy Dolls: Fashion clothes for the dolls of this period could be made from stamped fabric sold at sewing stores. Clothes could be cut and sewn by hand or by machine. The wardrobe shown is for an 11in (28cm) to 12in (31cm) doll such as the Vogue *Jeff*® or Mattel *Ken*®. The sportswear clothes are color coordinated so that many outfits can be created by mixing and matching.

    SEE: *Illustration 401.*
    PRICE: $10-15

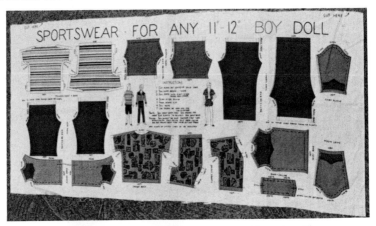

Illustration 401.

Illustration 402.

Coat Doll: Hollow plastic body and soft vinyl head; 30in (76cm); rooted, blonde straight hair; sleep eyes with eyelashes; feathered eyebrows; painted eyelashes under eyes; jointed at neck, shoulders, hips; 3rd and 4th fingers molded together but not curled; clothes not original; circa 1961.

    MARKS: "14//19c61" (back of neck)
    SEE: *Illustration 402. Beatrice Campbell Collection.*
    PRICE: $75-90

Girl in Playsuit: Hollow plastic body and soft vinyl head; 36in (91cm); sleep eyes with lashes; painted eyelashes under eyes; jointed at neck, shoulders, hips; 3rd and 4th fingers molded together and curled toward hand; blue printed playsuit; purchased by owner in Canada; circa 1961-63.
MARKS: "AE 3651" (head)
SEE: *Illustration 403. Beatrice Campbell Collection.*
PRICE: $65-80

Illustration 403.

Illustration 404.

Bride: Beautiful all-rigid vinyl body with soft vinyl head; 15in (38cm); "flat-type" face (like 14R dolls); big sleep eyes with lashes; closed-mouth; rooted hair; jointed at neck, shoulders, waist, hips; painted fingernails, toenails; individual fingers; high-heeled feet; unusually beautiful net over satin bride dress; crinoline underskirt; patterned nylon panties; trim around neck has shield-like embroidered panels; rhinestone bracelet, earrings, necklace, ring; trousseau included a gray knit skirt and top with pink and gray matching jacket; circa 1957-58.
MARKS: None
SEE: *Illustration 404. Inga Tomoletz Collection.*
PRICE: $35-45

Laurie: Rigid vinyl body, soft vinyl head and arms; 10½in (27cm); rooted dark blonde hair that can be washed and curled; blue sleep eyes with molded eyelashes; five black eyelashes painted at each side of eye; swivel waist; jointed at neck, shoulders, waist, hips; red lips, fingers and toenails; pierced ears; doll is the same as a *Little Miss Revlon*®, but there are no markings on the head; however, under right arm is a "10½ R" mark which is also on the *Revlon*® doll; clothes could be bought separately for *Laurie* and are of cheaper quality than the *Little Miss Revlon*® clothes; *Laurie* may have been dressed and marketed by a different company or Ideal may have sold this unmarked line to other stores; original outfit; pink rayon dress trimmed with pink lace; circa 1958.

Boxed Fashions: *Laurie* came with clothes that were sold in an oval plastic container marked "Laurie Ensembles/For *Laurie* and all/10½in (27cm) Teen Age Dolls."
Top (left to right)
1 White rayon dress with black, blue and pink circles and white shoes.
2. Gray rayon dress with pink braid, white flower and white shoes.
Bottom (left to right)
1. White rayon dress with black flocked design and black shoes.
2. Black net negligee.
3. Gray, white and yellow striped rayon dress, yellow pants and black shoes.
> **MARKS:** None on head; "10½ R" (under right arm)
> **SEE:** *Illustration 405.*
> **PRICE:** $35-40 (doll)
> $10-15 (boxed outfits)

Illustration 405.

Illustration 406.

Teen Boy: Rigid vinyl body, soft vinyl head; 10½in (27cm); similar to *Jeff*®, *Jill's*® boyfriend, by Vogue and *Bob*®, *Tinyteen's*® boyfriend, by Uneeda; molded hair painted light brown; blue sleep eyes with molded lashes; red lips; brown long curved eyebrows; jointed at neck, shoulders, and legs; 3rd and 4th fingers curved and molded together; clothes not original; circa 1958.
> **MARKS:** None
> **SEE:** *Illustration 406.*
> **PRICE:** $30

Revlon® is a registered trademark of Revlon, Inc.
Jeff® and *Jill*® are registered trademarks of Vogue Dolls, Inc.
Bob® and *Tinyteen*® are registered trademarks of the Uneeda Doll Co., Inc.

Valentine Dolls, Inc.

The registered trademarks, the trademarks and the copyrights appearing in italics within this chapter belong to Valentine Dolls, Inc., unless otherwise noted.

Perfect Patient: Plastic body with soft vinyl head; 13in (33cm); sleep eyes; came complete with crutches, bandages, toy hypodermic and candy pills; advertised in *Sears Christmas Catalog* of 1964.

This doll was a look-alike version of *Marybel®* by Madame Alexander (see page 39). In the Christmas catalog *Marybel®* was also advertised on the same page as *Perfect Patient*.

    MARKS: None
    SEE: *Illustration 407.*
    PRICE: $35-45 (Mint-in-box)

Chubby Checker Jan and Fran "Twisteen Sisters": 11½in (29cm) teenage doll; *Barbie®* look-alike; Valentine carried a complete line of "twist" outfits that fit this and other 11½in (29cm) teen dolls; 1962.

    SEE: *Illustration 408. Playthings*, March 1962.

Illustration 407.

Illustration 408.

Queen For a Day: Hard plastic body and vinyl head; 20in (51cm); sleep eyes; #693; wearing a full length formal gown of taffeta and nylon tulle; velvet robe has plush trim; doll walks and assumes life-like positions; 1957. "Doll seen daily on TV show of the same name."

    SEE: *Illustration 409. Toys and Novelties*, January 1957.

    PRICE: $45-55

Illustration 409.

DOLLS NOT PHOTOGRAPHED

    Valentine made many dolls for the mass market. Many of the "look-alike" dolls with no identification in the Sears & Roebuck catalog during the period from 1957 to 1965 were made by this company. They, too, made a *Barbie®* look-alike.

Barbie® Look-alike: Plastic with vinyl head; 11½in (29cm); jointed at neck, shoulders, waist, hips; high heels; circa 1961-1963.

    MARKS: Sometimes a "V" (head); other times no mark

Debbie Drake: Plastic with vinyl head; many joints for exercising; white rooted hair; painted eyes; molded lids; dressed in exercise outfit; circa 1963.

    MARKS: None on doll; "Debbie Drake" and "Valentine" (box)

Marybel® is a registered trademark of the Alexander Doll Co., Inc.   *Barbie®* is a registered trademark of Mattel, Inc.

Girl: One-piece stuffed vinyl.

MARKS: "AE 1406/46" (head); "v" (lower back)

Additional dolls in Valentine list for year 1962:

1. *Polly:* 11½in (29cm) high-fashion doll and clothes.
2. *Ballerina* doll.

These dolls were advertised in *Playthings,* March 1962.

Virga Company

The registered trademarks, the trademarks and the copyrights appearing in italics within this chapter belong to Virga Company.

Schiaparelli: During the 1950s doll wardrobes became very important. Designers in France and the United States designed beautiful clothes for different sizes of dolls. After Madame Schiaparelli had designed doll clothes for her delighted daughter, Gogo, she vowed she would enchant thousands of other little girls in the same way. In 1951 she designed clothes for the Effanbee Doll Co. and this advertisement appeared in the July issue of *Playthings.*

In the late 1950s she also designed clothes for Virga dolls. These costumes were well marked with a Schiaparelli label.

SEE: *Illustration 410. Playthings,* July 1951.

Illustration 410.   *Illustration 411.*   *Illustration 412.*

Doll in Lounging Clothes: Hard plastic body with soft vinyl head; 12in (31cm); reddish blonde rooted hair; sleep eyes with molded lashes; jointed at neck, shoulders, hips, above knees; fine detail on hands and high-heeled feet; 3rd and 4th fingers molded together and slightly curled; purple velvet pants and skirt which is lined with white, pink and purple rayon print; blouse matches lining of skirt; circa 1958-1960.

MARKS: "Virga" (head); "Schiaparelli" (tag in skirt)

SEE: *Illustration 411.*

PRICE: $40-50

Go-Go by Schiaparelli: Hard plastic body with soft vinyl head; 8in (20cm); head turning walker; closed-mouth; rooted pink hair; sleep eyes with molded lashes; crease in center of kneecap; standard arm hook (see *Hard Plastic Dolls,* page 2641); clothes designed by noted Paris designer Schiaparelli and marketed in distinctive "shocking pink" box; dress of pink satin with nylon pleated overskirt; pink flowers down the front of dress; pink pearls in her pink hair; pink stole; all original; 1956-1959.

MARKS: "Virga" (head)

SEE: *Illustration 412.*

PRICE: $75-85 (mint-in-box; higher prices have been paid for unusual dolls)
$25-50 (mint-in-box outfit; depending on the type)

Vogue Dolls, Inc.

The registered trademarks, the trademarks and the copyrights appearing in italics within this chapter belong to Vogue Dolls, Inc., unless otherwise noted.

Illustration 413.

Ginny Family:

One of the most fashionable dolls of the 1950s was *Ginny*. She was an 8in (20cm) hard plastic little girl. The later *Ginny* dolls had a vinyl head. *Ginny* had many outfits and accessories which could be purchased separately.

Later Vogue added various family members to the *Ginny* line. Each of these members came with clothes, furniture and accessories. These dolls were continued into the early 1960s.

In 1957 Vogue introduced *Jill* and *Ginnette*. *Jill* is *Ginny's* hard plastic teen sister. She had high-heeled feet. *Ginnette*, *Ginny's* sister, is an all-vinyl baby, 8in (20cm).

In 1958 the line was completed with the addition of *Jan*, *Jeff* and *Jimmy*. *Jan*, an all-vinyl high-heeled teen, is similar to *Jill* and gradually replaced *Jill*. *Jeff*, an all-vinyl teen, was *Jan* and *Jill's* boyfriend. *Jimmy*, an all-vinyl baby, 8in (20cm), was *Ginny's* new baby brother.

More information about *Ginny*, *Jill* and their fashions can be found in *Hard Plastic Dolls*, pages 245-256.

SEE: *Illustration 413. Toytime, 1958,* the Cleveland, Ohio, May Company Christmas Catalog.

Jeff: Rigid vinyl body and soft vinyl head; molded hair painted black; 11in (28cm); blue sleep eyes with molded lashes; jointed at neck, arms, hips; dressed in football uniform; beige pants; green jersey; 1958.

    MARKS: "Vogue" (head)
    SEE: *Illustration 414.*
    PRICE: $45-55

Illustration 414.

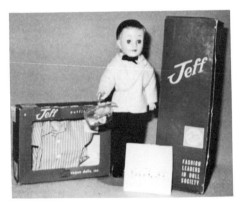

Illustration 415.

Jeff: For general characteristics, see *Illustration 414.* Dressed in tuxedo; white dinner jacket, black tie and pants; shown is *Jeff's* original brown box and fashion brochure; also included is an additional outfit that came in a brown box with a plastic window; the extra outfit is a pajamas set; 1958.

    MARKS: "Vogue" (head)
    SEE: *Illustration 415. Maybeth Manchook Collection.*
    PRICE: $50-60 (doll in box)
                   $20-30 (boxed outfit)

Jeff Brochure: TOP (left to right):
1. For skiing *Jeff* wears black felt ski pants, aqua sateen zipper jacket. Skis and poles included.
2. *Jeff's* car coat is made of water repellent beige nylon and fully lined. It has real buttonholes and toggle closings. Tweed Ivy League cap.
3. *Jeff's* dress suit is navy wool felt. With it he wears an oxford cloth shirt and bow tie.
4. *Jeff's* tuxedo suit has black pants with satin stripe, white dress shirt, white wool jacket, plaid cummerbund and tie. Corsage is for his date.

MIDDLE (left to right):
1. For school *Jeff* wears tan chino pants and a brown leather belt. His Ivy League striped shirt has three white snap buttons.
2. And so to bed...and *Jeff* wears his two-piece pajamas of beige broadcloth.
3. This is *Jeff's* colorful plaid bathrobe with tuxedo collar and sash belt.

BOTTOM (left to right):
1. *Jeff's* cabana suit has colorful swim trunks and matching shirt lined with yellow terry cloth. He wears scuffs.

2. For after school *Jeff* wears rugged blue jeans with a black belt and long sleeve black jersey sweater.
3. Summertime finds *Jeff* in gray Bermudas, black belt and bright red checked shirt. His knee-length socks are black jersey.
4. This smart tweed sport jacket can be worn with any of *Jeff's* slacks.
   SEE: *Illustration 416.*

Illustration 416.

Illustration 417.

Jill **and** *Jan:* *Jill* (left): Hard plastic; 10½in (27cm); sleep eyes; pierced ears; jointed knees; high-heeled feet; red painted lips, finger and toenails; dressed in black velvet formal, pink lace slip and pearl earrings; tagged outfit; *Jan* (right): rigid vinyl body and soft vinyl head; 10½in (27cm); blue sleep eyes; pierced ears; jointed at neck, shoulders, hips and waist; red lips, finger and toenails; brown rooted hair in a bubble cut; tagged outfit; black velvet bodice, white taffeta skirt trimmed in black velvet; white straw hat with black ribbon; painted green wood clothes closet; 1958.
   MARKS: *Jill* and *Jan* "Vogue" (head); *Jill* "Jill/Vogue Dolls/Made in USA/ c.1957" (back)
   SEE: *Illustration 417.*
   PRICE: $60-70 *Jill*
   $45-55 *Jan*

Jan and Jeff: For characteristics, see *Illustrations 414* and *417;* *Jan* (left): pink flocked nylon dinner dress trimmed with white lace; pink waist ribbon; *Jeff* (middle): black felt ski pants, aqua sateen zipper jacket, black pants with wood skis and poles; *Jan* (right): white raincoat with tie, matching hood trimmed with black corduroy; white purse; black shoes; circa 1958.
   MARKS: "Vogue" (on head of each doll)
   SEE: *Illustration 418.*
   PRICE: $45-55 *Jeff*
   $45-55 *Jan*

Illustration 418.

Illustration 419.

Jan and Jill Brochure (one of several issued). TOP (left to right):

1. Wonderful for school — this gay plaid cotton skirt, trim belt and white top plus a cuddly soft red cardigan with a golden pin.

2. A favorite of *Jan's* fashioned in bewitching blue cotton. The yoke and skirt banded with bold polka dots and frothy white lace.

3. Glamorous *Jill* wears cloud sheer black silk organza with pink tulle petticoat. Her lavish hat is party pink — her choker pearly pink.

4. *Jan* goes ice skating in red jersey leotard, swirling white felt skirt and short cropped jacket. She has a furry hat and white skates.

5. Against the sugary snow — *Jan* wears green felt pants and plaid bloused jacket. White ear muff cap, boots, mittens, skis and poles.

6. *Jan* could have danced all night — in her black velvet strapless wide-swirling skirt of frothy white lace. Full taffeta petticoat.

BOTTOM (left to right):

1. *Jill's* beautiful new-shape felt coat wraps and ties in front. In soft lemon yellow with matching flare brim cloche and clutch purse.

2. For stormy days, *Jill* wears this pretty hooded raincoat of clear vinyl lined with gay prints. She carries a matching tote bag.

3. *Jill* goes Western in her rodeo outfit of ranch blue twill trimmed with silver and black. Gun and holster set — white hat and boots.

4. *Jan's* Garden Party dress is sheer yellow organdy over whispery flowered taffeta. Aqua sash, choker, straw hat.

5. A truly lovely gown — bouffant nylon tulle over whispery pink taffeta traced with pink satin. Pink head-wreath, pearly choker.

6. How lovely *Jan* will be — dressed as a bride in cloud-white lace over gleaming satin. She wears a chapel length veil, carries bouquet.

    SEE: *Illustration 419.*

Illustration 420.

Jan and Jill Brochure (one of several issued); for additional clothes see *Illustrations 567-572, Hard Plastic Dolls;* TOP (left to right):

1. *Jill's* shirtwaist gem has a black and white cotton skirt and white taffeta blouse with roll-up sleeves. Cluster pleated skirt and belt.

2. Elegant harem-hemmed gown in swishy party pink. The strapless bodice is accented with waist high bow.

3. *Jill* relaxes after class in these blue denim jeans, yellow jersey and trim belt. She wears saucy glasses and golden hoops.

4. For gay summer nights, a party pink strapless fashioned in polished cotton with black beaded Cluny lace. Pearl white choker.

5. These reed slim Bermudas come in assorted plaids and are teamed with a white blouse and trim belt.

6. *Jill* is especially fond of this sheer red dotted swiss sundress. The skirt is lined for extra fullness and banded with white lace.

7. First choice for Spring — *Jill's* cropped top of white embroidered cotton and flary skirt of party pink.

8. *Jill* sets the pace with this cotton shirtwaist classic. Fashioned in yellow watercolor print with orange sash and roll-up sleeves.

BOTTOM (left to right):

1. For our pretty ballerina, flaring layers of white tulle with bodice of black sparkly

velvet. Pearly choker, silver crown and mask.

2. Fun in the sun when *Jan* wears this swimsuit with white piqué bodice and flaring plaid skirt. Dark glasses and terry towel.
3. Love those fringed pants and cropped top. *Jill's*, of course, in blue/green water color print. Jaunty straw sailor to match.
4. Another from *Jill's* wardrobe of cotton separates — an orange halter top with cluster pleated, all-over print skirt. Belt, too.
5. For *Jill's* leisure hours — black and white check slacks with belt, aqua cotton top and Oxford gray wool felt blazer.
6. Theatre Time — *Jill* wears this lavish aqua flowered taffeta with strapless bodice, harem-hem and aqua jacket.
7. Glamorous fireside fashions — these skinny pants and strapless top of black velvet. Bunny fur cloth shrug, choker, earrings.
   SEE: *Illustration 420.*

Illustration 421.

Jan: For general characteristics, see *Illustration 417;* this was a special series of costumed dolls from the early 1960s; *Jan* is costumed as *Frontier Days;* tag in dress reads "Vogue Dolls, Inc"; blue and yellow calico dress and bonnet; blue cotton apron; yellow shawl; white lace trim; black shoes; circa 1962.
   MARKS: "Vogue" (head)
   SEE: *Illustration 421.*
   PRICE: $50-60

Illustration 422.

Brikette: Plastic body and vinyl head and arms; 22in (56cm); green eyes; rooted orange hair; freckles; jointed at neck, waist, shoulders, hips; joint on waist is on ball attached to hips; black velvet top and white nylon skirt; replaced shoes and socks; 1959.
   MARKS: "Vogue Dolls, Inc.//
   ©1959" (bottom of upper body)
   SEE: *Illustration 422. Pat Parton Collection.*
   PRICE: $70-85

Brikette and Li'l Imp: Advertised in *Playthings,* August 1959, *Brikette;* 22in (56cm) with bending waist; sassy, freckle-face; emerald eyes; red-headed charmer. She is shown with her various costumes. *Li'l Imp;* 11in (28cm) saucy, freckle-faced Tomboy with twinkling, impish eyes and a roguish personality to match.

In 1964 a black *Li'l Imp* was added to the Vogue line.
   SEE: *Illustration 423 (Brikette).*
   Illustration 424 (Brikette in additional clothes and Li'l Imp).

Illustration 423.

Illustration 424.

Wee Imp: Hard plastic; 8in (20cm); special *Ginny* made in 1960 only; red hair; freckles; bending knee walker; had four matching outfits with *Li'l Imp*, the 11in (28cm) doll; dressed in shocking pink striped pants, top, nightcap; other costumes include blue jeans with red check cuffs and matching pants; dotted turquoise dress with lace trim; blue felt jumper-type dress with white tights and shirt, beret.
    MARKS: "Vogue" (head)
    SEE: *Illustration 425. Marge Meisinger Collection.*
    PRICE: $200-220 (boxed and brochure)

Love Me Linda: Vinyl head; hard plastic body; 15in (38cm); rooted hair; black eyes; eyelids similar to *Lonely Lisa®* (see *Illustration 369*); partial smile; white slash at edge of eye; gray eye shadow above lids; painted eyes; slender body and legs; flat feet; 1965.
    MARKS: "Vogue Doll//©1965"
    SEE: *Illustration 426. Laura May Brown Collection.*
    PRICE: $25-35 (all original)

Angel Dolls: By the late 1950s Arranbee had become a division of the Vogue Doll Company. They made many sizes of "Angel" dolls. See pages 73 and 74. Some of the earlier dolls such as the *Littlest Angel* were marked "R & B," but later ones were usually marked "Vogue Dolls." Sometimes they also were dated. For complete information, check the Vogue and Arranbee sections of this book.

Littlest Angel: Semi-soft vinyl; 11in (28cm); sleep eyes with molded lashes; dimples over individual fingers; dimples on knees; red fat cheeks on face; jointed at neck, shoulders, hips; dimples on knees; came with other outfits; 1964.
Center doll on left: dressed in yellow cotton pants and top with daisy trim on both pants and top; green velvet ribbon is stem of daisy; lace trim; brunette pigtails.
Center doll on right: dressed in mock suede red dress with white piqué yolk; black braid trim.
    MARKS: "VOGUE DOLL//1964" (head); clothes have no tags
    SEE: *Illustration 427* (two dolls in center).
    PRICE: $35-45

Littlest Angel: Hard vinyl head and arms, plastic body and legs; 14½in (36cm); rooted hair in several styles and colors; sleep eyes with real lashes; smiling face with closed-mouth; dimples on shoulders; dimples on knees; individual fingers; came with other outfits; 1965.
Doll on left: dressed in yellow knit jumpsuit with white knit blouse.
Doll on right: red, blue, black and white Scotch plaid dress with white sleeves and neck.
Lonely Lisa® is a registered trademark of the Royal Doll Co.

Clothes are marked: "Vogue Dolls, Inc.//Made in U.S.A."
MARKS: "Vogue Doll//c1965" (head)
SEE: *Illustration 427* (taller dolls on each side).
PRICE: $35-45

Illustration 425.

Illustration 426.

Illustration 427.

DOLLS NOT PHOTOGRAPHED

Miss Ginny: 16in (41cm); jointed at neck, shoulders, waist, hips; wardrobe includes:
1. Red and white candy-stripe pinafore dress and straw skimmer.
2. Yellow cotton dress with velvet sash.
3. Flowered aqua jersey knit slacks and kerchief, felt top.
4. White satin-trimmed embroidered eyelet dress.
5. Hooded fleece jacket and hot pink cord pants.
6. Party dress of rose-trimmed velvet with nylon skirt, matching bonnet, lace petticoat.
There were matching *Ginny* dolls available; 1962-1963.

Ginny: Plastic and vinyl; 36in (91cm); walking doll; wardrobe included jeans, red checked shirt; natural straw hat; turquoise cotton cord long pants and middy top with jersey insert; nylon sheer white party dress, taffeta petticoat, crimson short jacket of velveteen, 1960.
This is the same doll as *My Angel Walking Doll*® by Arranbee. (See *Illustration 88.*) Each doll came with a *Ginny* doll with a matching outfit.
PRICE: $100-135 (doll alone; no *Ginny*)

My Angel Walking Doll® is a registered trademark of the Arranbee Doll Company.

Identification Section

All of the names in *italics* appearing in the following section are protected names. The legal protections were left off for the readability of the charts and price guide.

HH-high heeled
MH-medium heeled

DOLLS BY HEIGHT

3in (8cm)
1. Marx *Doll House Girl*

3½in (8cm)
1. Marx *Doll House Boy*

3¾in (10cm)
1. Ideal *Little Princess Girl*

4in (10cm)
1. Ideal *Little Princess Boy*

5in (13cm)
1. Marx *Doll House Mother*

5½in (14cm)
1. Ideal *Little Princess Mother*
2. Marx *Dollhouse Father*

6in (15cm)
1. Commonwealth *Dress-Me Dolls*
2. Doll Bodies *Dress-Me Dolls*
3. Ideal *Little Princess Father*
4. Kenner *Kati*

7in (18cm)
1. Hollywood *Little One*
2. Horsman *Michel*
3. Horsman *Jane*

7½in (19cm)
1. Child *Lilli* HH
2. Hong Kong *Lilli* HH

8in (20cm)
1. Alexander *Little Lady*
2. Commonwealth teen doll HH
3. Commonwealth girl doll
4. Cosmopolitan *Cha Cha Heel* MH
5. Cosmopolitan *Ginny* all-vinyl type
6. Cosmopolitan *Little Miss Ginger* HH
7. Deluxe *Penny Brite*
8. Eegee *Shelly*
9. Horsman *Peggy Petite*
10. Ideal *Salty and Pos'n Salty*
11. Nancy Ann *Muffie* all-vinyl
12. Virga *Schiaparelli* HH
13. Vogue *Ginny* HP with vinyl head

8½in (22cm)
1. Effanbee *Official Girl Scout Doll*
2. Nancy Ann *Miss Nancy Ann*

9in (23cm)
1. American Character *Cricket*
2. Commonwealth teen HH
3. Commonwealth adult walking doll HH
4. Ideal *Pepper and Pos'n Pepper*
5. Mattel *Skooter* and *Ricky*
6. Model Toys teen doll HH
7. Mollye *Perky*
8. Plastic Molded Arts *Little Miss Joanie* HH

10in (25cm)
1. Active teen doll HH
2. Alexander *Cissette* HH
3. Belle *Little Margie*
4. Commonwealth adult HH
5. Eegee *Little Miss Debutante* HH
6. Effanbee *Mickey*
7. Nancy Ann *Miss Nancy Ann* HH
8. Sayco *Miss America* HH
9. Uneeda *Blue Fairy* HH
10. Uneeda *Pollyanna* HH

10½in (27cm)
1. A & H *Gigi* HH
2. Admiration *Miss Francie* HH
3. American Character *Toni* HH
4. Arranbee *Miss Coty* HH
5. Beehler Arts teen doll HH
6. Cosmopolitan *Miss Ginger* HH
7. Effanbee *Mickey*
8. Hoyer, Mary *Vicki* HH
9. Horsman *Cindy* HH
10. Ideal *Little Miss Revlon* HH
11. Laurie teenage doll HH
12. Mayfair of Canada *Debbie* HH
13. P (in circle) teen doll HH
14. Plastic Molded Arts teen doll HH
15. Remco *Libby Littlechap*
16. Rosebud soft vinyl doll
17. Uneeda *Tiny Teen* or *Suzette* HH
18. Uneeda *Sally Starr* HH
19. Unique teenage doll HH
20. Unknown teen boy
21. Vogue *Jill and Jan* HH

11in (28cm)
1. Alexander *Frederich*
2. Alexander *Gretel*
3. Alexander *Kurt*

4. Alexander *Marta*
5. Arranbee *Littlest Angel*
6. Commonwealth HH
7. Effanbee *Fluffy*
8. Effanbee *Mickey*
9. Sayco *Miss America*
10. Vogue *Littlest Angel*
11. Vogue *Jeff*

11½in (29cm)
1. A & H *Marcie* HH
2. American Character *Mary Makeup* HH
3. Debbie Toy Debbie HH
4. Eegee *Babette Suzette* HH
5. Elite *Bonnie* HH
6. Elite *Wendy* HH
7. Fab-Lu *Babs* HH
8. Fab-Lu *Bill*
9. Fab-Lu *Randy*
10. German *Lilli* HH
11. Hong Kong *Lilli* HH
12. Horsman *Cinderella*
13. Horsman *Patty Duke* MH
14. Mattel *Barbie* HH
15. Nasco *Hello Dolly* HH
16. Reliable teenage doll HH

12in (31cm)
1. Alexander *Brenda Starr* HH
2. Alexander *Katie*
3. Alexander *Pamela* MH
4. Alexander *Yolanda* HH
5. American Character *Misty* HH
6. American Character *Popi* HH
7. American Character *Tressy* HH
8. Eegee *Andy*
9. Eegee grow hair
10. Hasbro *G.I. Joe*
11. Hong Kong *Lilli* HH
12. Horsman *Mary Poppins*
13. Ideal *Mitzi* HH
14. Ideal *Samantha the Witch* HH
15. Ideal *Shirley Temple*
16. Ideal *Tammy and Pos'n Tammy*
17. Mattel *Ken and Allen*
18. Mollye *Perky*
19. P & M *Paula May* HH and Flat
20. Palitoy (English) *Mary Make-up* HH
21. Palitoy (English) *Tressy* HH
22. Pedigree *Sindy* HH
23. Ross *Tina Cassini* HH
24. Royal *Joy*
25. Unique *Elly Mae Clampett* HH
26. Virga *Schiaparelli* HH

12½in (32cm)
1. Gilbert *James Bond*
2. Ideal *Mom* MH

13in (33cm)
1. Ideal *Dad*
2. Valentine *Perfect Patient*

13½in (34cm)
1. Remco *Lisa Littlechap*

14in (36cm)
1. Alexander *Little Orphant Annie*
2. Alexander *Liesel*
3. Alexander *Louisa*
4. Alexander *Maria* MH
5. American Character *Betsy McCall*
6. American Character *Caroline* look alike
7. American Character *Preteen Tressy*
8. American Character *Toni* HH
9. Effanbee *Little Lady*
10. Ideal *Miss Revlon* HH
11. Juro *Rags to Riches* HH
12. Roddy *Beauty Queen* HH

14½in (37cm)
1. Horsman *Tweedie*
2. Vogue *Littlest Angel*

15in (38cm)
1. Active HH
2. Alexander *Caroline*
3. Belle bride
4. Bonomi girl
5. Eegee *Gemmette*
6. Effanbee vinyl *Patsy*
7. Effanbee *Suzette*
8. General Foods *Linda Williams*
9. Horsman *Betty*
10. Ideal *Shirley Temple*
11. Marx *Miss Seventeen*
12. Remco *Father Littlechap*
13. Remco *Mother Littlechap* MH
14. Uneeda *Vermont Maid* HH
15. Vogue *Love Me Linda*

16in (41cm)
1. Alexander *Edith the Lonely Doll*
2. Alexander *Kelly*
3. Alexander *Marybel*
4. Alexander *Pollyanna*
5. Allied Grand ponytail
6. Effanbee *Girl Scout*
7. Gladtoy *Poor Pitiful Pearl*
8. Horsman *Poor Pitiful Pearl*
9. Horsman *Little Miss Moppet*
10. Uneeda *Coquette*
11. Vogue *Little Miss Ginny*

16½in (42cm)
1. Alexander *Elise* MH HH

17in (43cm)
1. Active HH
2. Alexander *Elise*
3. Alexander *Leslie* MH
4. Alexander *Maggie Mixup*
5. Alexander *Mary Ellen Playmate* MH
6. Alexander *Maria* MH
7. Alexander *Polly* MH
8. Arranbee *Angel*
9. Effanbee *Miss Chips*
10. Ideal *Shirley Temple*
11. Ideal stuffed vinyl girl
12. Natural *Miss Ritzi* HH

18in (46cm)
1. Active HH
2. Alexander *Elise* MH HH
3. Alexander *Patti*
4. Arranbee *My Angel*
5. Effanbee *Junior Miss* HH
6. Effanbee *Honey Walker* MH HH
7. Effanbee *Suzie Sunshine* and *Schoolgirl Writing Doll*
8. Effanbee *Telle Belle*
9. Eegee *Luv-able Skin* HH
10. Eugene *My Little Lady* HH
11. 14R type HH
12. Horsman *Couturier Cindy*
13. Ideal *Revlon* HH
14. P & M *Paula May* HH and Flat
15. Sayco *Miss America* HH

19in (48cm)
1. Eegee *My Fair Lady* HH
2. Effanbee *Honey Walker* HH
3. Effanbee *Jr. Miss Bride* HH
4. Effanbee *Little Lady*
5. 14R HH
6. Horsman *Renee Ballerina* HH
7. Horsman *Cindy* HH
8. Sayco stuffed vinyl doll HH
9. Rite Lee *Miss Lynn* HH
10. Uneeda *Dollikins Miss Twist* HH
11. Uneeda mature doll HH

20in (51cm)
1. Admiration bride HH
2. American Character *Toni* HH
3. Deluxe Reading *Candy*
4. Doll Bodies HH
5. Effanbee *Jr. Miss* HH
6. Effanbee *Honey Walker* MH
7. Effanbee *Little Lady*
8. Eugene *My Little Lady*
9. 14R HH

10. Ideal *Revlon* HH
11. Juro *Rags to Riches* HH
12. Laurel *Gabby*
13. M.C. Doll Co. HH
14. Mattel *Chatty Cathy*
15. Natural *Angela Cartwright*
16. Petitcollin *Marie Ange*
17. Plastic Molded Arts *Glamour Doll* HH
18. Royal *Lonely Lisa*
19. Valentine *Queen for a Day*

21in (53cm)
1. Alexander *Jacqueline*
2. American Character *Whimsey*
3. Brevete *GeGe*
4. Deluxe Reading *Nancy Nurse* HH
5. Eegee *Tandy Talks*
6. Effanbee *Honey Walker* HH
7. Kasam HH
8. Nasco *Hello Dolly* HH
9. Royal Girl
10. Royal *Robin*

22in (56cm)
1. Alexander *Edith the Lonely Doll*
2. Alexander *Kelly*
3. Alexander *Melinda*
4. Alexander *Pollyanna*
5. American Character *Betsy McCall*
6. Vogue *Brikette*

22½in (57cm)
1. Eegee *Puppetrina*

23in (58cm)
1. Alexander *Sweetie Walker*
2. Ideal *Revlon* HH
3. Sayco *Bride*
4. Sayco all-latex girl

24in (61cm)
1. Allied *Grand Bonnie Bride* HH
2. Arrow HH
3. Citro *Polly Ponds*
4. Deluxe *Bride* and *Princess* HH
5. Effanbee *Alyssa*
6. Effanbee *Bud*
7. Electrosolids *Ellie Echo*
8. Natural *Miss Anniversary*
9. Royal girl

25in (64cm)
1. Allied Grand bride HH
2. American Character *Toni* HH
3. American Character *Toodles*
4. Deluxe Reading bride HH
5. Horsman *Jackie* HH
6. Horsman *Cindy*
7. Laurel *Penny* HH

26in (66cm)
1. Active HH
2. Arranbee *My Angel*
3. Juro *Dick Clark*
4. P & M *Paula Mae* HH

28in (71cm)
1. Deluxe Reading HH
2. Eegee stuffed vinyl HH
3. Effanbee *Boudoir Doll*

29in (74cm)
1. Alexander *Barbara Jane*
2. Deluxe Premium *Betty the Beautiful Bride* HH

30in (76cm)
1. Alexander *Betty*
2. Alexander *Mimi*
3. American Character *Little Miss Echo*
4. Natural *Angela Cartright*
5. Unknown 30in (76cm)

31in (79cm)
1. Alexander *Penny*
2. Uneeda *Pollyanna*

32in (81cm)
1. Debbie *Debbie Walker*
2. Eegee *Susan Stroller*
3. Effanbee *Mary Jane*
4. Uneeda *Freckles*
5. Uneeda *Princess from Babes in Toyland*

36in (91cm)
1. Alexander *Joanie*
2. American Character *Betsy McCall*
3. American Character *Linda McCall*
4. Arranbee *My Angel Walking Doll* (same doll as Vogue *Ginny*)
5. Disney, Walt *Mary Poppins*
6. Horsman *Cindy*
7. Ideal *Daddy's Girl*
8. Ideal *Patty Playpal*
9. Ideal *Shirley Temple*
10. Lorrie girl
11. Uneeda *Betsy McCall*
12. Vogue *Ginny* (same doll as *My Angel Walking Doll* by Arranbee)

38in (97cm)
1. American Character *Sandy McCall*
2. Ideal *Lori Martin*
3. Ideal *Peter Playpal*

42in (107cm)
1. Ideal *Daddy's Girl*

MARKS 1

1. A on lower hip .... Arrow, Deluxe, Allied
2. A1 .... Deluxe Reading
3. A1 HH .... Deluxe Reading
4. A1 HH H92 .... Deluxe Reading
5. A1 HH K70 .... Deluxe Reading
6. A.C. .... American Character
7. AE 18 .... Hoyer, Mary
8. AE 23 .... Hoyer, Mary
9. AE (see Marks 2 list page 235)
10. AE (see Marks 3 list page 237)
11. Amer. Char. .... American Character
12. B5 12 .... Ideal
13. B5 12½ .... Ideal
14. BS 12 .... Ideal
15. BS 12½ .... Ideal
16. BS 12 .... Ideal
17. BS 12½ .... Ideal
18. B 18 .... Horsman
19. DO 9-E .... Ideal
20. E G .... Eegee
21. F .... Fab Lu (possible)
22. G 9 .... Ideal
23. G 9W .... Ideal
24. G 9E .... Ideal
25. G 42-1 .... Ideal
26. H .... Horsman
27. J.K. 25 .... Horsman
28. K .... Nasco, Gilbert, Kaysam
29. K.T. .... Allied
30. M 12 .... Ideal
31. M 12E .... Ideal
32. M 13 2 .... Ideal
33. MC .... Bonomi
34. N.F. .... Uneeda
35. O-H .... Eegee
36. Ⓟ .... See list page 184
37. PL .... Natural
38. P9-3 .... Ideal
39. P.M.A. .... Plastic Molded Arts
40. R & B .... Arranbee
41. s (small) .... Sayco
42. SG .... Deluxe Reading (possible)
43. ST 12 .... Ideal
44. ST 12N .... Ideal
45. T 12E .... Ideal
46. 2T 18 .... Ideal
47. U 18 .... Vermont Maid, Uneeda
49. U 22 .... Vermont Maid, Uneeda
50. U 26 .... Vermont Maid, Uneeda
50. U .... Uneeda
51. V (large or small) .... Valentine
52. V 15 .... Valentine
53. VP 17-Z .... Ideal
54. VT 10½ .... Ideal
55. VT 18 .... Ideal
56. VH .... Deluxe Reading

57. VH 25 2 .... Deluxe Reading
58. VH 25 19 .... Deluxe Reading
59. VW .... Valentine
60. W1 .... Commonwealth
61. W 12 .... Ideal
62. W 13 L .... Ideal

MARKS 2

1. 2H .... Eegee
2. 2S .... Uneeda
3. 5 N.F. .... Uneeda
4. 5 SG .... Deluxe Reading (possible)
5. 6 .... Deluxe Reading
6. 8 .... Effanbee
7. 10 .... Effanbee
8. 10 .... Ideal
9. 10½ under arm .... Ideal
10. 12 .... Ideal
11. 12/5 .... Eegee
12. 13 .... Uneeda
13. 14R .... See page 104
14. 14R 1 .... Eegee
15. 15 BAL HH .... Belle
16. 15 P .... Eegee
17. 15 N.. Ideal
18. 18 .... Horsman, Mary Hoyer
19. 19 .... Unique, Mary Hoyer
20. 21 .... Arrow
21. 21 HH K74 .... Deluxe Toys
22. 23 .... Mary Hoyer
23. 25 .... Horsman
24. 25 H7 .... Deluxe Reading
25. 26 .... Vermont Maid
26. 52 .... Arrow
27. 63 .... American Character
28. 67 .... Miss Echo (see page 69)
29. 74 .... Arrow
30. 82 .... Horsman
31. 83 .... Horsman
32. 86 .... Deluxe Reading
33. 88 .... Horsman
34. 155 .... Deluxe Reading
35. 190 .... Deluxe Reading
36. 251//AE .... Deluxe Reading
37. 251//AE//90 .... Deluxe Reading
38. 251//AE//Y29 .... Eegee
39. 251//AE//100 .... Deluxe Reading
40. 767 .... Bonomi
41. 818 .... Horsman
42. 1406/46 .... Valentine
43. 2112 .... Allied
44. 4274 K .... Kaysam
45. 4595 .... Citro
46. 5320 .... Kaysam
47. 6211 .... Horsman
48. 6618 .... Horsman

MARKS 3
AE

The dolls that have an AE mark can be attributed to many different doll companies. These companies purchased both parts and completed dolls from Artistic Doll Co.//Eastern Doll Corp. (See *Illustration 428*). This advertisement was in the March 1958 issue of *Toys and Novelties*. Usually these dolls were of a less expensive quality and retailed to a mass market.

Companies using the AE mark included Eegee, Nasco, New Dolly Toy Company, Valentine, P & M Sales, Deluxe Reading and its satellite companies, Valentine, Unique and others. Catalog outlets such as Aldens, and retail stores such as W. T. Grant also assembled dolls for sale. The 14R-type dolls are attributed to this company.

Their most common type doll was the high-heeled lady doll. However, they also made the large Playpal-type doll as well as babies and others. Many of these dolls were sold with AE markings or no marks on either the dolls or their boxes. However, the authors have seen AE marked dolls in boxes with the name of most of the above companies.

IDENTIFICATION OF DOLLS BY BODY CHARACTERISTICS
HAIR — DOLLS WITH UNUSUAL HAIR CONSTRUCTION.

1. Alexander *Pamela* — had velour strip to hold three changes of wigs
2. Alexander *Polly* — chignon with formal dresses
3. Alexander *Brenda Starr* — came with instruction book for hair care
4. American Character *Tressy* — grow hair which operates with key turning a button on body
5. American Character *Pre-teen Tressy* — grow hair; operates with button on body
6. Arranbee *Coty Girl* — came with instruction book for hair styling
7. Eegee — grow hair girl; operates with button on body
8. Kenner *Electric Mold Master* — molds for wigs
9. Mattel *Miss Barbie* — 3 wigs over molded hair
10. Mattel *Fashion Queen Barbie* — 3 wigs
11. Pedigree 1964 catalog shows 21 different hairstyles used for dolls. Examples include "Petal-cut," "Roman-bob," plaited hair in chignon, ponytail, cascade and princess style.

JOINTED LIMBS ON DOLLS
Jointed Ankles

1. Alexander *Elise*
2. Alexander *Mimi*
3. American Character *Betsy McCall* 22in (56cm)
4. American Character *Toni* 25in (64cm)
5. Effanbee *Honey Walker* (a few)

Illustration 428.

Jointed Arms and Wrists

1. Alexander *Elise* arms
2. Alexander *Maggie Mixup*
3. Alexander *Mimi* wrists
4. American Character *Betsy McCall* 22in (56cm) wrists
5. Deluxe Toy Co. *Candy* elbow
6. Horsman *Couturier* type of ball-jointed elbows

Jointed Knees and Thighs

1. Alexander *Brenda Starr*
2. Alexander *Elise*
3. Alexander *Jacqueline*
4. Alexander *Mimi*
5. Arranbee and Vogue *Littlest Angel*
6. Deluxe Toys *Candy*
7. Effanbee *Honey Walker*
8. Hasbro *G.I. Joe*
9. Plastic Molded Arts *Miss Joan*
10. Sayco *Miss American Pageant*
11. Vogue *Ginny*
12. Vogue *Jill*

Barbie® Look-Alike Dolls

It did not take the doll industry very many months to realize that the little girls were very enthusiastic about *Barbie*. Even today the toy stores are full of both *Barbie* dolls and *Barbie* look-alikes. The phenomena is still strong after more than one quarter of a century.

The dolls listed below were made to compete with the early *Barbie in the years 1957 to 1965:*

1. A & H *Marcie*
2. Allied
3. American Character *Tressy*
4. Alexander *Brenda Starr*
5. Debbie Toys *Debbie*
6. Eegee teen dolls including *Babette*
7. Elite *Wendy*
8. Elite *Bonnie*
9. Fab Lu *Babs*
10. German *Lilli*
11. Hong Kong *Lilli*
12. Ideal *Mitzi*
13. Ideal *Grown-up Tammy*
14. Ideal *Misty*
15. Ideal *Samantha the Witch*
16. Marx *Miss Seventeen*
17. Nasco *Hello Dolly*
18. Reliable of Canada teen doll
19. Ross Oleg Cassini's *Tina Cassini*
20. Uneeda *Suzette* in two sizes
21. Valentine *Jan and Fran Twisteens*
22. Valentine *Debbie Drake*

Tammy® Look-Alike Dolls

1. Deluxe Reading *Penny Brite*
2. Eegee grow hair doll
3. Fab-Lu *Randy*
4. Horsman *Cinderella*
5. Horsman *Elizabeth Taylor* in *Bluebird*
6. Horsman *Mary Poppins*
7. Horsman *Patty Duke*
8. Hoyer, *Mary Vicki*
9. Pedigree *Sindy*
10. Unique *Calico Lass*
11. Unique *Elly May Clampett*

POSEABLE DOLLS

1. Alexander *Polly*
2. Alexander *Mary Ellen Playmate*
3. American Character *Betsy* has "Magic Flex" joints
4. American Character *Tressy* and *Mary Makeup*
5. American Character *Cricket*
6. Ideal *Pos'n Tammy, Grown Up Pos'n Tammy, Pos'n Pepper, New Pos'n Pepper, Pos'n Ted, Pos'n Pete and Pos'n Salty*

STUFFED VINYL

All stuffed vinyl were made to be posed. That is why they are often found in poor condition today.

1. American Character *Whimseys*
2. Citro *Polly Pond*
3. Deluxe Reading *Betty Bride* and many others
4. Eegee *Luv-able*
5. 14R high-heeled doll
6. Gladtoy and Horsman *Poor Pitiful Pearl*
7. Horsman *Renee Ballerina* and some of the other *Couturier* dolls
8. Rite-Lee *Miss Ritzi*
9. Royal *Robin* and similar dolls

SWIVEL WAIST DOLLS

1. A & H *Gigi*	10½in	(27cm)
2. Alexander *Mimi*	30in	(76cm)
3. Alexander *Melinda*	16in	(41cm)
4. American Character *Betsy McCall*	14in	(36cm)
5. American Character *Betsy McCall*	20in	(51cm)
6. American Character *Sweet Sue Sophisticate*	20in	(51cm)
7. American Character *Toni*	25in	(64cm)
8. Arranbee *Coty Girl*	10½in	(27cm)
9. Arrow girl	24in	(61cm)
10. Brevete *GeGe*	21in	(53cm)
11. Commonwealth teenage girl Style D101	10in	(25cm)
12. Cosmopolitan *Miss Ginger* — rigid vinyl bodies only	10½in	(27cm)
13. Deluxe Reading high-heeled girl	24in	(61cm)
14. Eegee *My Fair Lady*	19in	(48cm)
15. Eegee *Little Miss Debutante* and other high-heeled sizes	10in	(25cm)
16. Effanbee *Jr. Miss*	19in	(48cm)
17. 14R some dolls only	19in	(48cm)
18. Hasbro *G.I. Joe*	11in	(28cm)
19. Horsman *Cindy*	19in	(48cm)
20. Horsman *Cindy*	10½in	(27cm)
21. Hoyer, Mary *Vicki*	10½in	(27cm)
22. Ideal *Revlon*	20in	(56cm)
23. Ideal *Revlon*	18in	(46cm)
24. Ideal *Little Miss Revlon*	10½in	(27cm)
25. Juro *Rags to Riches*	20in	(51cm)
26. *Laurie* Doll	10½in	(27cm)
27. Mayfair of Canada *Debbie*	10½in	(27cm)
28. Natural *Miss Ritzi*	17in	(43cm)
29. Plastic Molded Arts *Miss Joan*	11in	(28cm)
30. Sayco *Miss America*	10in	(25cm)
31. Uneeda *Suzette* and *Tiny Teens*	10½in	(27cm)
32. Uneeda *Dollikins*	19in	(48cm)
33. Valentine *Twisteen* Sisters	11½in	(29cm)
34. Vogue *Jan*	10½in	(27cm)
35. Vogue *Brikette*	22in	(56cm)

TALKING DOLLS

1. Eegee *Tandy Talks*
2. Effanbee *Belle Telle*
3. Electrosolids *Ellie Echo*
4. Laurel *Gabby* — Could be purchased speaking Spanish.
5. Laurel *Gabby Jane* — Could be purchased speaking Spanish.
6. Laurel *Fashion Doll* — Could be purchased speaking Spanish.
7. Laurel *Penny* — Could be purchased speaking Spanish.
8. Mattel *Charming Chatty*
9. Mattel *Chatty Kathy*

WALKING DOLLS

1. Alexander *Betty Walker*
2. Alexander *Joanie*
3. Alexander *Sweetie Walker*
4. Arranbee *My Angel Walking Doll*
5. Cosmopolitan *Ginger*
6. Cosmopolitan Cha Cha Heeled *Ginger*
7. Debbie Doll Company *Debbie* Walker
8. Disney, Walt *Mary Poppins* (large doll)
9. Eegee *Susan Stroller*
10. Effanbee *Mary Jane*
11. Horsman *Cindy* (larger size)
12. Laurel *Gabby Jane*
13. Natural *Angela Cartwright*
14. Natural *Miss Anniversary Doll*
15. Valentine *Queen for a Day*
16. Vogue *Little Imp*
17. Vogue *Ginny* 8in (20cm) and 36in (91cm)

Ÿ MARK ON LOWER BACK

The following companies have one or more dolls with thie Ÿ:

1. Deluxe Reading
2. Arrow
3. Bell
4. General Foods
5. Horsman
6. Mattel
7. Valentine

For a picture of this mark, see *Illustration 611*, page 282 in *Hard Plastic Dolls*.

IDENTIFICATION OF DOLLS BY TRENDS AND FASHIONS
1957-1965
BEAUTY QUEENS

Beauty pageants were not new during this period. However, television brought the excitement and glamour into living rooms. Often families and friends gathered to cheer their state's representative, and the little girls and their mothers dreamed of competing.

Sayco Doll Company capitalized on this dream.

1. *Miss America*, 18in (46cm) (see *Illustration 370*).
2. *Miss America*, 10in (25cm) (see *Illustration 371*).
3. *Miss America Beauty Pageant*, 10¾in (27cm) (see *Illustration 372*).

The small chubby *Miss America Beauty Pageant* had a large wardrobe which captured the fashions and trends of the time. Sayco also offered a contest and the main prize was a trip to the September Miss America contest in Atlantic City for the little girl and her mother. An entry blank for the contest was in the brochure which came with each doll.

Uniforms for women were becoming popular and they offered WAC and WAVE uniforms as well as a TWA hostess uniform.

Miss America was expected, by this time, to be proficient in some sports. The chubby doll sported skating, ski, terry cloth bathing suit and jodphur outfits.

The All-American girl also had clothes for school, for nursing and for becoming a "farmerette."

The tiny doll, which looked like its "mother," also could go to balls, weddings and school parties. In addition, it could play "school," like untold generations have done before and since.

But most of all, the doll was a real "Queen."

Another beauty pageant winner was *Miss Seventeen*, a very sophisticated teenager by Marx. (See *Illustration 261*.) She, too, had a complete wardrobe.

For the adult generation, the television "Queen For a Day" was very popular. It was the dream of the women of this generation to be selected a queen on this program. They received gifts and a special day of activities. Valentine provided some of the glamour with their *Queen For a Day* doll. (See *Illustration 409*.)

On the throne of England was the young and glamorous Queen Elizabeth II. The world watched this lovely lady and Madame Alexander created some of the most beautiful dolls of all time. She continued this tradition with *Cissy, Cissette* and *Elise*.

Roddy of England also made a 14in (36cm) *Miss England*. She was a *Cissy* look-alike.

BRIDES

Wedding gowns were not a new trend for dolls, but the popularity of bride dolls remained strong during this period. The details of the wedding dresses for dolls follow closely those of the grown-up bride.

1. Admiration
2. Alexander *Cissy, Cissette, Elise, Polly*
3. Allied Grand *Bonnie*
4. American Character *Toni, Sweet Sue Sophisticate, Whimsey*
5. Arranbee *Coty Girl*
6. Belle
7. Deluxe Reading *Betty the Beautiful Bride*
8. Effanbee *Jr. Miss, Miss Chips*
9. Fab-Lu *Babs*
10. Horsman *Cindy*
11. Ideal *Miss Revlon*
12. Mattel *Barbie* (in first wardrobe)
13. Marx *Miss Seventeen*
14. Royal
15. Vogue *Ginny, Jill, Jan*

CARTOONS AND COMICS

1. Alexander
2. American Character
3. German doll
4. Horsman and Gladbrook

Brenda Starr, Penny
They used comic books for advertising their dolls.
Lilli in Bild newspaper
Poor Pitiful Pearl

DOLLS RELATED TO COSMETICS, PERFUME AND HAIR CARE

1. Alexander *Cissy*
2. Alexander Character *Little Lady*
3. American Character *Misty*
4. American Character *Misty*
5. American Character *Mary Makeup*
6. American Character *Tressy*
7. Arranbee *Miss Coty*
8. Citro *Polly Ponds*
9. Effanbee *Little Lady*
10. Hasbro *Dotty Darling*
11. Horsman *Tweedie*
12. Ideal *Revlon Dolls*
13. Ideal *Toni*
14. Ideal *Harriet Hubbard Ayer*
15. Mattel *Color 'N Curl*
16. Palitoy of England *Mary Makeup*

Yardley Perfume
Little Lady Toiletries, Helene Pessl, Inc.
Miss Clairol Hair Color
Various kinds of makeup
Various kinds of makeup
Various kinds of makeup
Coty Cosmetics
Ponds Cosmetics
Little Lady Toiletries, Helene Pessl, Inc.
Miniature Plastic Cosmetics
Tweedie
Revlon Cosmetics
Toni Home Permanents
Harriet H. Ayer Cosmetics
Hair care
Cosmetics and hair color

The American Character *Tressy* and *Mary Makeup* and the Ideal *Harriet Hubbard Ayer* had a pale face so little girls could practice applying makeup.

In England Palitoy also had a *Mary Makeup*.

COUTURIER AND DESIGNER CLOTHES

1. Banbury Coats	Horsman *Tweedie* and Ideal *Shirley Temple*
2. Oleg, Cassini	Ross Products *Tina Cassini*
3. Continental fashions — Italy	Bonomi girl
4. Copies of Couturier Fashions	Fab Lu *Babs, Bill, Randy*
5. Couturier Division	Horsman *Cindy, Renee Ballerina*
6. Geisha Robes and Lounging clothes	Horsman *Tweedie*
7. Fashion Institute of Technology by Jay E. Watkins and Edward Roberts	Marx *Miss Seventeen*
8. Love Dress	Horsman *Tweedie*
9. Mr. John Junior Hats	Horsman *Tweedie*
10. Paris designed dresses and hairstyles	Petitcollin *Marie Ange*
11. Regan Swimwear	Horsman *Tweedie*
12. Schiaparelli	Virga walking doll and high-heeled teenage doll *GoGo*

DOLL BODIES THAT ARE OVERSIZED

The sales of very large "companion-sized" dolls became very popular by 1958-1959. In 1960 the Chanel Plastics Industries announced that they had made the technical advances needed to produce a 40in (102cm) doll. This was a four-year-old size. This new size was available for the Christmas line of various manufacturers.

SEE: *Illustration 429. Toys and Novelties*, October 1960.

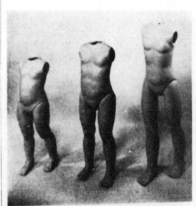

THREE SIZES of doll bodies show the growth of dolls. From left to right, 30", 36" and the new four-year-old size, 40". This new 40" size will make its appearance during the coming Christmas Season as a result of technical advances made by Chanal Plastics Industries, custom blow molders, in Rego Park, Long Island, New York.

Illustration 429.

REAL AND MAN-MADE FUR FOR DOLL CLOTHES

Fur has been used for cold weather clothing throughout history. After World War II, new man-made fur material such as Borgana was made available to clothing manufacturers. It was very popular because it looked and felt like fur and was popularly priced. It also did not need the care and storage of real fur. Little girls loved the "real" man-made new fur. Their dolls liked it, too.

For collectors and dealers trying to authenticate clothing found in boxes and trunks, here is a list of dolls and the fur they wore.

1. American Character *Toni*	Muff, hat, stole
2. Arranbee *Coty Girl*	Hat, muff
3. American Character *Angel*	Hat, muff
4. Brevete *GeGe*	Short fur coat, leopard coat
5. Eegee *Luv-a-ble*	Trim on collar and hat
6. Eugene Dolls high-heeled doll	Jacket, hat, bag
7. 14R dolls — high-heeled doll	Many different outfits including short jackets, Persian lamb full coats, hats
8. Mary Hoyer *Vicki*	Fur stole
9. Ideal *Revlon*	Fur stole
10. Ideal *Tammy*	Fur trim on ski outfit
11. Mattel *Barbie* (first wardrobe)	Stole, mink cuffs and hat, ermine stole. Mattel used both real and man-made fur.
12. Mattel *Chatty Cathy*	Trim on coat and hat
13. Miss *Nancy Ann*	Fur collar and muff
14. Natural high-heeled doll	Fur coat, hat, muff
15. P & M high-heeled doll	Muff
16. Plastic Molded Arts	Advertised real mink stoles
17. Remco *Lisa Littlechap*	Fur-trimmed suede coat
18. Ross *Tina Cassini*	Bunny fur hat, collar, muff used on ski outfit
19. Sayco *Miss America Pageant Doll*	White rabbit fur coat, muff, hat
20. Valentine *Queen for a Day*	Plush mock fur on robe
21. Virga *Schiaparelli*	Pink fur stole

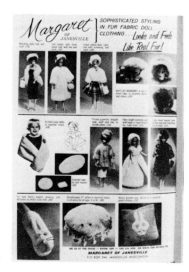

Margaret of Janesville, Wisconsin, advertised in *Toys and Novelties*, "Sophisticated Styling in Fur Fabric Doll Clothing... Looks and Feels like Real Fur." Available were "chubby" coats, long coats, three-quarter length coats, floor length evening cape, leopard coats, stoles, hats, muffs. She also made stuffed animals from the same materials.

SEE: *Illustration 430. Toys and Novelties*, March 1964.

Illustration 430.

PERSONALITY DOLLS

1. Julie Andrews	*Mary Poppins* Horsman and *My Fair Lady* Eegee
2. Angela Cartwright	"Danny Thomas Show" Linda Williams Natural Doll Company
3. Carol Channing	*Hello Dolly* Nasco, Kaysam
4. Dick Clark	"Bandstand" Juro
5. Donna Douglas	"Beverly Hillbillies" Elly Mae Clampett, Unique
6. Patty Duke	Horsman
7. Carolyn Kennedy	Alexander, American Character
8. Jacqueline Kennedy	Alexander, Horsman
9. Shari Lewis	Alexander
10. Gigi Perreau	*Gigi* A & H Doll Company
11. Juliet Prowse	*Gigi* Kaysam
12. Shirley Temple	Ideal
13. Trapp Family	Alexander

DOLLS WITH TELEPHONES

The "teenage craze" grew during these years. Thanks to television, teenagers around the country could see the trends as they watched "Bandstand," "Andy Hardy" and other movies. Once they discovered that the new "Princess" phone could be available for their private use, they begged for the popular item for birthdays and Christmas. Patty Duke popularized the phenomena, and the doll manufacturers added the telephone as an accessory.

1. Deluxe Reading *Penny Brite*
2. Effanbee *Belle Telle*
3. Electrosolids *Ellie Echo*
4. Horsman *Patty Duke*
5. Ideal *Tammy Ring-a Ding* outfit with Princess phone
6. Ideal *Pos'n Tammy* with her own telephone booth
7. Kenner *Electric Mold Master Girl's Set* mold for telephone
8. Mattel *Barbie Suburban Shopper* and *Baby Sitter*. The first Mattel telephones had a metal dial. This was quickly replaced with plastic.
9. Mattel *Skipper Dreamtime* outfit included a phone

RADIOS

1. Fab Lou *Randy* transistor radio with *Beach Outfit*
2. Ideal *Tammy* radio came with *Cutie Co-ed* outfit
3. Kenner *Electric Mold Master Girl's Set* mold for miniature radio

PHONOGRAPH

1. Hasbro *Karen* miniature phonograph and records

Angel

#17614 17" **Angel**, 6-piece all vinyl girl with rooted short bob hair dressed in red organdy dress with wide lace trim.
List $6.00

#17624 17" **Angel**, 6-piece all vinyl girl with rooted side-part bob dressed in yellow polished cotton shirtwaist trimmed with lace and black belt.
List $6.00

#17714 17" **Angel**, 6-piece all vinyl girl with rooted short bob dressed in aqua print taffeta dress with lacy white nylon collar and mob cap.
List $7.00

#17724 17" **Angel**, 6-piece all vinyl girl with rooted short bob dressed in bright plaid cotton dress with puffy white blouse and red velvet hat.
List $7.00

#17814 17" **Angel**, 6-piece all vinyl girl with rooted short bob dressed in black and white check coat with black velvet collar and hat over coral taffeta dress with black belt and coral pocketbook.
List $8.00

#17824 17" **Angel**, 6-piece all vinyl girl with rooted pony tail dressed in bridal gown of white Point D'Esprit skirt over white satin with filmy veil topped by pearl tiara.
List $8.00

#21814 21" **Angel**, 6-piece all vinyl girl with rooted side-part bob dressed in plaid cotton dress with red felt bodice and hat.
List $8.00

#21824 21" **Angel**, 6-piece all vinyl girl with rooted short bob dressed in flowered nylon dress over aqua underskirt.
List $8.00

#21954 21" **Angel**, 6-piece all vinyl girl with rooted pony tail dressed in red cord jacket and pants with white fur collar and hat.
List $9.00

ALL DOLLS WILL BE SHIPPED IN ASSORTED HAIR COLORS

Illustration 90. A page from an R & B catalog showing a page of *Angel* dolls. See page 74.

Illustration 153A. Ellie Echo. The Famous Tape Recorder Doll. See page 102.

Illustration 153C. Wendy. See page 102.

Illustration 142. Girl in Pink Dress by the Eegee Goldberger Doll Mfg. Company. *Susan Schroeder Collection.* See page 95.

Illustration 340. Marie Ange, the Petitcollin doll from France. *Sears Catalog from the Elizabeth Poole Collection.* See page 188.

INDEX

Updated Price Guide

The following is an updated list of values for the dolls described in this book. Prices in this updated guide — as throughout the book — reflect a range of prices from various parts of the United States. The prices are only given for the specific dolls photographed. These dolls would be in good to *mint* condition and include original clothes. Unless stated in the price section, there would be higher prices for a doll with an original box, tag and/or "tissue" mint conditions. Local prices will vary, and often this variance will be considerable.

If a doll is scarce or very rare, it will be costly. Where dolls are still "coming out of the attics" or "readily available at garage sales," prices will be lower. Personality dolls are usually more expensive.

Because clothes were an important part of society in the late 1950s and early-to-mid 1960s, these dolls had elegant and lovely clothes. Even everyday clothes were fancy and surprisingly well made. As with all dolls, unusual clothes will add to the quoted prices. Undressed dolls are usually 1/4 to 1/3 the value of a dressed doll.

The rigid vinyl, vinyl, and plastic dolls in this book were still available in quantity five or six years ago. Today the collector sees fewer and fewer in mint condition and most prices have risen — but not all of them. It is not at all uncommon to see unheralded, rare dolls go for remarkable prices at auction, especially when in mint condition. A comparison of the prices in this updated list to the prices in the original 1987 text provides dramatic evidence of the changing values of these very fashionable dolls.

A & H DOLLS
  Gigi: (Illustration 3) $35-40 (all original)
  Marcie: (Illustration 4); doll alone $15; wardrobe set $35-40
ACTIVE DOLL CORP.
  Teenage Doll: (Illustration 5) $25-35
ADMIRATION TOY CO., INC.
  Bride: (Illustration 6) $25-40
  Miss Francie: (Illustration 7) $45-50
ALEXANDER DOLL CO., INC.
  Barbara Jane: (Illustration 8) $375-400 (If doll is discolored, price will be considerably lower.)
  Betty: $375-400
  Brenda Starr: (Illustrations 26 and 27); doll $150-175; outfits $50-75
  Caroline: (Illustration 22, center) $300-350
  Caroline: (Illustration 24); doll $300-350; rare boxed sailor outfit $100-150; regular boxed outfits $75-125
  Cissette: (Illustration 16); rare buble cut *Cissette*, made for one year only $275-300+
  Cissy: (Illustration 10); in street clothes $250-300; in formal dresses $350-700

CoCo: (Illustration 13) $2000-2200
Edith, the Lonely Doll: (Illustration 17, right); 16in (41cm) $275-335; 22in (56cm) $320-375
Elise: (Illustration 12); doll $175-200; boxed clothes $60-70; Alexander shoes alone $7-10
Elise: (Illustration 15); not enough price samples available
Elise and *Maggie Mixup:* boxed outfits $70-100
Elise Ballerina: (Illustration 14) $200-225 (depending on costume)
Elise Bridesmaid: (Illustration 11) $275-300+
Jacqueline: (Illustration 22, left) $600-700
Jacqueline: (Illustration 22, right) $600-700
Jacqueline: (Illustration 23); *Jacqueline* alone $600-800; *Caroline* alone $350-400; set $1100-1400; boxed outfit for *Jacqueline* $250-275; boxed outfit for *Caroline* $125-150
Joanie: (Illustration 30) $350-375
Katie: (Illustration 30) $350-375
Kelly: (Illustration 17, left); 16in (41cm) $300-325; 22in (56cm) $325-375

Kurt: (Illustration 28) $650-700+ (very few sample prices)
Leslie: (Illustration 34); street clothes $350-375; formals $400-450
Leslie: outfits $100-150 (mint-in-box)
Little Lady: $800+
Little Orphant Annie: (Illustration 31) $375-400
Maggie Mixup: (Illustration 20) $300-350
Mary Ann: $75-315 (doll is still made)
Marybel: (Illustration 18); doll $175-200; doll in case $300-350
Mary Ellen Playmate: $325-350
Melinda: 14in (36cm) and 16in (41cm) $350-370; 22in (56cm) $375-395
Mimi: (Illustration 21) $400-475+ (The Tyrolean costume and other special costumes may command a higher price.)
Pamela: (Illustration 25); in case with extra clothes $1000-1100; boxed clothes $175-225
Patti: $350-375
Penny: (Illustration 9) $300-375 (If doll is discolored, price will be considerably lower.)
Polly: outfits $100-150 (mint-in-box)
Pollyanna: (Illustration 19) $350-400+
Polly Ballerina: (Illustration 33, right) $300-350
Polly Bride: (Illustration 32) $325-375
Polly in Ball Gown: (Illustration 33, left) $350-400
Sound of Music: (Illustration 29) $2500 set
Sweetie Walker: $175-200
Yolanda: doll $250-300

ALLIED-GRAND DOLL MFG., INC.
Bonnie Bride: $35-50
Toddler: (Illustration 35) $45-50

AMERICAN CHARACTER DOLL CORPORATION-AMERICAN DOLL AND TOY CORPORATION
Betsy McCall: (Illustration 51) $250-275+ (hard to find)
Betsy McCall: (Illustration 54) $250-275
Blue Ribbon Doll: (Illustration 77) $35-50
Caroline Kennedy Look-alike: (Illustration 76) $100-125 (in original clothes)
Cricket: (Illustration 68) $40-60 (depending on costume)
Little Miss Echo: (Illustrations 78 and 79) $150-175
New Tressy (Magic Make-up Face): (Illustration 65) $40-45
New Tressy Fashion Shop: (Illustration 66) $100-110

Popi: (Illustrations 72 and 73); doll in box $30; costume packet $10
Pre-teen Tressy: (Illustrations 70 and 71) $100-125 (rare doll)
Sweet Sue Sophisticate Bride (Toni®): (Illustrations 48 and 49) $200-225
Toni®: (Illustration 37); doll $70-90 (depending on costume); boxed outfit $40-65
Toni®: (Illustration 38) $85-110 (depending on costume)
Toni®: (Illustration 39) $100-110 (depending on outfit)
Toni®: (Illustration 40) $45-50
Toni®: (Illustration 45) $200-225
Toni®: (Illustration 46) $200-225
Toni®: (Illustration 47) $200-225
Toni®: (Illustration 50) $235-250
Toodles with Peek-a-Boo Eyes: (Illustration 80) $200-220 (with original clothes)
Tressy: (Illustration 57) $75-90 (mint-in-box)
Tressy dolls: (Illustration 55, left) $45-55; (Illustration 55, right) $40-45
Tressy Fashions: (Illustration 60), In the Swim $40-45; (Illustration 61), Surprise Party $50-55
Tressy (first): (Illustration 56) $50-60
Tressy Hair Glamour Paks and Brochure: (Illustration 62); hair care kits $25-30
Whimsies: (Illustration 74) $100-120
Whimsies: (Illustration 75) $100-120

ARRANBEE DOLL COMPANY
Angel: (Illustration 90) $80-90 (depending on outfit)
Coty® Girl Doll: (Illustration 81); doll and box $115-130; doll $80-100; boxed outfit $45-60
Coty® Girl Doll: (Illustration 82); doll $115-130; boxed outfit $45-60
Coty® Girl Doll Brochure: (Illustration 83); boxed outfits $45-60
Coty® Girl Doll Brochure: (Illustration 84); boxed outfits $20-25
Coty® Girl Doll Brochure: (Illustration 85); boxed outfits $25-30
Littlest Angel: (Illustration 86) $50-75+ (depending on outfit)
My Angel: (Illustration 87, top row) $55-75 (depending on outfit)
My Angel: (Illustration 87, middle and bottom row) $65-80
My Angel Walking Doll: (Illustration 88) $80-90
My Angel Walking Doll: (Illustration 89); doll alone, no Ginny®, 8in (20cm) $100-135

ARROW

Doll in Orange Dress: (Illustration 91, left); $75-95; (Illustration 91, right) $80-100 (mint condition)

BEEHLER ARTS, LTD.

High Heel Doll: (Illustration 92) $15

BELLE DOLL AND TOY CORP.

Bride: (Illustration 93) $70-75

Margie: (Illustration 94) $80-85

BONOMI (ITALY)

Girl: (Illustration 97) $45-50

BREVETE GEGE OF FRANCE

GeGe: (Illustration 98) $100-125 (depending on outfit)

BROOKGLAD CORP.

Poor Pitiful Pearl: $45-50

CITRO

Polly Pond's® Beauty Doll: (Illustration 102) $80-90 (with box)

COSMOPOLITAN TOY & DOLL CORPORATION

Ginger Grows Up with Cha Cha Heel: (Illustration 106) $80-90+ (rare)

Ginger with Cha Cha Heels and Little Miss Ginger: (Illustration 115); *Cha Cha* on left $60-75 (rare); *Little Miss Ginger* on right $60-70

Little Miss Ginger: (Illustration 114) $85-100

Miss Ginger: (Illustration 107) $275-300 pair

Miss Ginger: (Illustration 108, left) $85-110; (Illustration 108, right) $80-90

Miss Ginger: (Illustration 109, left) $75-85; (Illustration 109, right) $80-90

Miss Ginger: (Illustration 110, left and right) $75-85; (Illustration 110, middle) $85-110

Miss Ginger Brochure: (Illustrations 111 and 112); boxed outfit $45-65

DEBBIE TOY COMPANY

Debbie Doll: (Illustration 117) $20-25

Debbie Walker: (Illustration 116) $125-135

DELUXE READING

Betty the Beautiful Bride: (Illustration 120) $85-100

Bride: (Illustration 121) $60-75

Bride: (Illustration 122) $85-95

Bride: (Illustration 124) $75-80

Candy Fashion: (Illustration 118) $90-110

Girl in Pink Hat: (Illustration 119) $85-95

Penny Brite: (Illustration 125) $20-25 (in box)

Princess: (Illustration 123) $75-80

DOLL BODIES COMPANY

Lu-Ann: (Illustration 131) $20-45 (depending on costume)

EEGEE GOLDBERGER DOLL MFG. CO., INC.

Andy: $20-25

Annette: $20-25

Barbie® Look-alike: (Illustrations 138 and 139) $60-70

Gemettes: $35-40 (all original with ornaments)

Girl in Pink Dress: (Illustration 142) $50-60

Grow-hair Doll: (Illustration 140) $60-70

Little Miss Debutante: (Illustration 137) $50-75 (mint condition)

Luv-able Skin Doll: (Illustrations 133 and 134) $125-150 (mint condition only)

My Fair Lady: (Illustrations 135 and 136) $150-200

Puppetrina: (Illustration 141) $65-75

Shelley: (Illustration 136) $20-30

Susan Stroller: (Illustration 143); 32in (81cm) $85-100

Tandy Talks: $50-60

EFFANBEE DOLL CORPORATION

Belle-Telle and Her Talking Telephone: (Illustration 152) $100-135 (in operating condition)

Fluffy Official Campfire Bluebird Doll: (Illustration 149, left) $85-100

Honey Walker: (Illustration 146) $150-200+ each

Jr. Miss Bride: (Illustration 147) $80-100

Little Lady: (Illustration 144); not enough samples of doll in original box with toiletries to price; $30-50 (good condition; not in original clothes)

Mary Jane: (Illustration 148) $200-250

Mickey: (Illustration 145); *Mickey Baseball Player, Mickey Sailor, Mickey Football Player, Mickey Baseball Player* $115-125 (mint-in-box); $80-100 (mint); $25-50 (played with condition)

Miss Chips Bride: (Illustration 153) $85-100

Official Girl Scout #11-956: (Illustration 149, doll on right) $40-45

Patsy Ann: (Illustration 150) $125-150

Suzie Sunshine: (Illustration 151); various prices depending on year of production and costume.

ELECTROSOLIDS CORPORATION (ELSCO)

Ellie Echo, the Famous Tape Recorder Doll: (Illustration 153A); not enough samples available.

ELITE CREATIONS INC.

Bonnie: (Illustration 153B) $20-25

Wendy: (Illustration 153C) $20-25

EUGENE DOLLS
  My Little Lady: (Illustration 154); 18in (46cm) with fur jacket $50-55; 20in (51cm) with fur jacket $60-70
14R DOLLS
  Girl in Black Fur Coat: (Illustration 155) $60-80
  Girl: (Illustration 156) $50-60
  Teenage Girl: (Illustration 157) $25-30
FAB-LU LIMITED
  Babs: (Illustration 158) $100-120 (mint-in-box)
  Bill: (Illustration 158) $80-100 (mint-in-box)
  Outfits: (Illustration 158) $20 (mint-in-box)
  Randy the Teen Age Girl Doll: (Illustration 168) $25-35
GENERAL FOODS
  Linda Williams: (Illustration 170) $40-50 (in original outfit only)
GILBERT, MANUFACTURED BY IDEAL TOY COMANY, MARKETED BY GILBERT
  James Bond 007: (Illustration 171) $200-225+ (original in box)
GLADTOY TOY COMPANY, BROOKGLAD CORP.
  Poor Pitiful Pearl: (Illustrations 172 and 173) $45-55
HASBRO, HASENFIELD BROS. INC.
  Dolly Darlings: (Illustration 175) $15-18 (in case)
HOLLYWOOD DOLL MANUFACTURING COMPANY
  Little One: (Illustration 176); all original in picture frame box $30-40; doll alone $10-15
HORSMAN DOLLS, INC.
  Cindy: (Illustration 177) $75-85
  Cindy: (Illustration 180) $75-85
  Cindy: (Illustration 181) $75-85
  Cindy: (Illustration 182); doll in original box $85-95; doll $60-70
  Cindy Bride: (Illustration 178) $110-125
  Couturier Dolls: (Illustration 184) $50-75 (all original in mint condition); $25-50 (original but poor vinyl)
  Couturier's Lady: (Illustration 183) $100-125 (all original in mint condition); $25-50 (original but poor vinyl)
  Couturier's Renee Ballerina: (Illustration 185) $50-55 (all original in mint condition); $20-25 (original but poor vinyl)
  Jackie: (Illustrations 188 and 189) $185-200 (in original clothes)
  Patty Duke: (Illustration 195) $60-70 (with picture and telephone)

  Poor Pitiful Pearl: (Illustration 190) $80-100 (with brochure)
  Mary Poppins: (Illustration 193) $45-60 each
  Mary Poppins and Friends: (Illustration 192); *Mary Poppins* $35-50; *Mary Poppins* in box $75-85; *Michael,* hard to find $25-35; *Jane,* hard to find $25-35; set $95-100; set in gift package, complete $145-165
  Tweedie: (Illustration 186) $15-75 (depending on outfit)
  Tweedie: (Illustration 187) $25-30
  Walt Disney's Cinderella: (Illustration 194); set in gift package, complete $145-165
IDEAL TOY CORP.
  Betsy McCall: (Illustration 242a) $400-500 (depending on costume)
  Daddy's Girl: $125-145
  Girl: $80-100
  Glamour Misty The Miss Clairol® Doll: (Illustration 224); boxed set $90-125
  Grown-up Tammy: (Illustration 223) $50-60 each
  Little Miss Revlon®: (Illustration 206); doll in box $130-150; doll $90-120; boxed outfit $50-70
  Little Miss Revlon®: (Illustration 207); doll in box $130-150; doll $90-120; boxed outfits $50-70
  Little Miss Revlon®: (Illustration 208) $90-120
  Little Princess Doll House Dolls: (Illustration 243) $65+ (rare)
  Lori Martin: $100-135
  Mitzi: (Illustration 242b) $60-80 (depending on outfit)
  Mom and Dad (part of Tammy's family): (Illustration 225); doll $60-65; doll in box $70-75
  New Pepper: (Illustration 228) $25-35 either doll
  Patti Playpal: (Illustration 238) $220-250
  Patti Playpal: (Illustration 240) $220-250
  Pepper: (Illustration 226); $30-45 (in box)
  Pepper and Dodi: (Illustration 229) $25-35
  Peter Playpal: (Illustration 241) $350-385
  Pos'n Pepper: (Illustration 227); 45-60 (in box)
  Pos'n Salty: (Illustration 230); $60-70 (in box)
  Pos'n Tammy and her Telephone Booth (No. 9105-8): (Illustration 222) $70-80
  Revlon® Doll: (Illustration 199) $160-200
  Revlon® Doll: (Illustration 200) $160-200
  Revlon® Doll: (Illustration 201) $90-110
  Revlon® Doll: (Illustration 203) $160-180

Revlon® Doll Bride: (Illustration 202) $160-200

Shirley Temple: (Illustration 216); 12in (31cm) $140-165 (depending on costume); 15in (38cm) $250-300 (all original, mint and depending on costume)

Shirley Temple: (Illustration 219) $1650-1750+ (mint-in-box)

Shirley Temple in red coat: (Illustration 217) coat $60

Tammy: (Illustration 220) $45-75 (depending on costume)

Ted (Tammy's brother), Tammy, Pos'n Tammy: (Illustration 221) $35-65 (depending on costume)

JURO NOVELTY CO., INC.

Rags to Riches Doll: (Illustration 245) $75-85 (complete)

KAYSAM-JOLLY TOY CORPORATION

Girl with High Heels: (Illustration 247) $40-60 (original costume)

LAUREL DOLLS, INC.

Penny the Fashion Doll: (Illustration 249) $55-75 (more if Spanish speaking)

Gabby Baby: (Illustration 249) $35-45 (more if Spanish speaking)

Gabby Jane: (Illustration 249) $55-75 (more if Spanish speaking)

Gabby Linda: (Illustration 249) $50-65 (more if Spanish speaking)

LILLI (BILD LILLI OF GERMANY)

Lilli: (Illustrations 251 and 252); 11½in (29cm) blonde with newspaper, mint-in-tube $1300-1500; 11½in (29cm) brunette or redhead with newspaper, mint-in-tube $2000+; 11½in (29cm) blonde, no tube $700+; 11½in (29cm) brunette or redhead, no tube $1000+; 7½in (19cm), mint-in-tube $700-900; 7½in (19cm), out-of-tube $500+

LILLI LOOK-ALIKES

Hong Kong Lilli: (Illustration 256) $175-200 (in this costume)

Hong Kong Lilli: (Illustration 257) $125-150

Hong Kong Lilli: (Illustration 258) $70-80

Hong Kong Lilli: (Illustration 259) $70-80

M.C. DOLL COMPANY

Teenage High-Heel Doll: (Illustration 260) $45-50 (depending on costume)

MARX (LOUIS MARX & CO., INC.)

Doll House Family: (Illustration 265); set $35-50

Miss Seventeen — a Beauty Queen: (Illustration 261); complete with box $135-175; doll in original outfit alone $85-100

Miss Seventeen Wardrobe Packaged in a Fashion Book: (Illustrations 262 and 263); boxed clothing $35-50

MATTEL, INC.

Allan: (Illustration 297) $175-265 (mint-in-box); $75-145 (mint-out-of-box)

Barbie: (Illustration 279) #3 *Barbie* $700-1200 (mint-in-box); #3 *Barbie* $425-675 (mint-out-of-box); *Silken Flame* $135-200 (mint-in-package); *Winter Holiday* $135-175 (mint-in-package)

Barbie: (Illustration 285); outfits only, mint-in-package; *Evening Splendor* $155-255; *Enchanted Evening* $200-325

Barbie: (Illustration 288); outfit only, *Barbie Baby Sits* $230-350 (mint-in-package)

Barbie: (Illustration 300) $500-1200 (mint-in-box); $355-600 (mint-out-of-box)

Barbie #1: (Illustration 266) $3000-4400+ (mint-in-box); $1500-2500+ (mint-out-of-box)

Barbie #1 in Gay Parisienne Outfit: (Illustrations 267, 268 and 269); outfit only $1400-1500 (mint-in-package), $1000-1250 (mint-out-of-package)

Barbie #2 and Barbie #3: (Illustration 271, left) *Barbie #2* $2500-4500 (mint-in-box), $1500-2500 (mint-out-of-box); (Illustration 271, right) *Barbie #3* $700-1000 (mint-in-box), $350-700 (mint-out-of-box)

Barbie #2 and Barbie #4: (Illustration 274, left) *Barbie #2* $2500-4000 (mint-in-box), $1500-2500 (mint-out-of-box); (Illustration 274, middle) *Barbie #4* $400-650 (mint-in-box), $200-300 (mint-out-of-box)

Barbie #5: (Illustration 275) $400-600 (mint-in-box); $200-300 (mint-out-of-box)

Barbie 1959: (Illustration 270); *Gay Parisienne* $900-1400 (mint-in-package), $600-700 (mint-out-of-package); *Roman Holiday Outfit* $900-1200 (mint-in-package), $600-700 (mint-out-of-package); *Easter Parade* $900-1200 (mint-in-package), $600-700 (mint-out-of-package)

Barbie 1960: (Illustration 272); outfits only, mint-in-package; *Solo in the Spotlight* $175-275; *Silken Flame* $100-150; *Busy Girl* $150-225; *Enchanted Evening* $250-325; *Let's Dance* $110-175

Barbie 1962: (Illustration 280); *Solo in the Spotlight*, outfit only with all accessories including microphone $175-300 (mint-in-package)

Barbie and Friends: (Illustration 289) $350-425

Barbie and Ken: (Illustration 282); outfits only, mint-in-package; *Ski Queen* $150-225; *Ski Champion* $125-200

Barbie and Ken: (Illustration 287); outfits only, mint-in-package; *Nurse* $175-275; *Doctor* $150-225

Barbie and Ken: (Illustration 292); outfits only, mint-in-package; *Stewardess* $250-375; *Pilot* $250-375

Barbie & Ken Little Theatre Brochure: (Illustration 293); outfits only, mint-in-package; *Cinderella* $175-275; *Prince* $175-275; *Red Riding Hood and Wolf* $125-150; *King Arthur* $225-350; *Guinevere* $200-300; *Barbie Arabian Nights* $200-300; *Ken Arabian Nights* $200-300

Charmin' Chatty: (Illustration 309) $120-130

Charmin' Chatty: (Illustration 310); outfit $50-60

Charmin' Chatty Let's Play Nurse: (Illustration 311); outfit $50-60

Chatty Cathy: (Illustration 303, left) $70-95

Chatty Cathy: (Illustration 303, right) $70-95

Chatty Cathy Patterns: (Illustration 308) $10 each

Color Magic Doll and Costume Set: (Illustration 301); blonde hair *Barbie* $800-1300 (mint-in-box); brunette hair *Barbie* $1000-1500 (mint-in-box)

Fashion Queen Barbie: (Illustration 284) $250-525+ (mint-in-box)

"Junior-Edition" styles for Skipper, Barbie's Little Sister: (Illustration 296); outfits $30-95 (mint-in-package)

Ken: (Illustrations 277 and 278) $200-350 (mint-in-box); $145-200 (mint-out-of-box); tuxedo $175-250 (mint-in-package)

Midge (Barbie's Girlfriend): (Illustration 283) $150-225 (mint-in-box); $75-135 (mint-out-of-box)

Miss Barbie: (Illustration 291) $350-700 (mint-in-box with all accessories, furniture, etc.)

Molded Hair Ken: (Illustration 286) $150-200 (mint-in-box); $55-75 (mint-out-of-box)

New Chatty Cathy: (Illustration 303, center) $60-80

New Chatty Cathy: (Illustration 307) $60-80

Ricky: (Illustration 299) $175-250 (mint-in-box); $75-150 (mint-out-of-box)

Skipper (Barbie's Little Sister): (Illustration 295) $175-250 (mint-in-box); $75-135 (mint-out-of-box)

Skooter: (Illustration 298) $175-275 (mint-in-box); $75-135 (mint-out-of-box)

Swirl Ponytail Barbie: (Illustration 290) $350-500 (mint-in-box); $175-350 (mint-out-of-box)

Unusual Barbies Wearing "Fashion Queen" Swimsuit: (Illustration 302); brunette Swirl *Barbie* $350-700 (mint-in-box); blonde Ponytail *Barbie* $200-350 (mint-in-box)

M.G.M. SALES, INC.

Perky: (Illustration 312) $30-40 (depending on costume)

Perky: (Illustration 313) $30-40 (depending on costume)

NANCY ANN STORYBOOK DOLLS, INC.

Miss Nancy Ann: (Illustration 316) $85-110

Miss Nancy Ann: (Illustration 317) $85-110

Miss Nancy Ann: (Illustration 318) $85-110

Miss Nancy Ann: (Illustration 319) $85-110

Miss Nancy Ann (smaller version): (Illustration 320) $80-100

NASCO (SEE ALSO KAYSAM)

Carol Channing: (Illustration 322) $45-50

Hello, Dolly Doll: (Illustration 321) $175-200 (in box)

NATURAL DOLL CO., INC.

Angela Cartwright Doll: (Illustration 327) $135-145 (very few sample prices available)

Doll in Fur Coat: (Illustration 325) $60-80 (depending on costume)

Miss Anniversary: (Illustration 324) $50-60

Ⓟ

ⓅHigh-Heeled Dolls: (Illustrations 333 and 334) $15-30

Sally Starr: (Illustration 335) $55-70

P & M DOLL COMPANY INC.

Paula Mae: (Illustration 337) $65-75

PLASTIC MOLDED ARTS

Girl in Leotard: (Illustration 339) $15 each

PETITCOLLIN

Doll from France — Marie Ange: (Illustration 340) $35-65

PRINCESS ANNA DOLL CO., INC.

Princess Anne: (Illustration 340A) $25-35 (in box, depending on costume)

REMCO INDUSTRIES

Littlechap Family: (Illustrations 341-349); *John Littlechap* $50-55; *Lisa Littlechap* $50-55; *Judy Littlechap* $30-35; *Libby Littlechap* $30-35

ROSEBUD

Scotch Girl in Kilts: (Illustration 350) $45-50

ROSS PRODUCTS, INC.

Tina Cassini: (Illustrations 351 and 352) $75-100 (mint-in-box); $50-60 (out-of-box, depending on outfit)

ROYAL DOLL CO.

Joy in a Raincoat: (Illustration 365) $30-35 (depending on costume)

Joy as a Bride: (Illustration 366) $30-35 (depending on costume)

Joy in France: (Illustration 367) $30-35 (depending on costume)

Lonely Lisa: (Illustration 369) $50-75

Robin: (Illustration 368) $35-45

SAYCO DOLL COMPANY

Glamour Girl Bride: (Illustration 380) $60-75

Miss America Doll: (Illustration 370) $90-100

Miss America Pageant Doll: (Illustration 371) $50-80 (depending on costume)

Miss America Pageant Doll: (Illustration 373); *TWA Hostess* doll in original outfit $50-55

Miss America Pageant Doll: (Illustration 374); doll in original outfit $50-55

Miss America Pageant Doll — Wave: (Illustration 372); doll including box and brochure $80-100; outfits $30-50

Teenager in Red Striped Dress, Style #20B: (Illustration 379); doll and box $35-45 (depending on costume)

UNEEDA DOLL CO., INC.

Barbie® Look-alikes: (Illustration 392); *Suzette* $50-60

Barbie® Look-alikes: (Illustration 393); *Suzette and Eegee* $50-60

Betsy McCall: (Illustrations 389 and 390); doll in box $100-125

Blue Fairy: (Illustration 381) $75-90 (mint)

Coquette: (Illustration 395) $35-45

Girl in Green Dress: (Illustration 387) $65-75

Girl in Red Dress: (Illustration 386) $65-75

Miss Twist: (Illustration 391); doll in street clothes $60-75; cocktail dresses, formals, velvet pedal pushers with nylon blouse $50-60; unusual outfits $70

Pollyanna: (Illustration 384) $55-70

Pollyanna: (Illustration 385) $100-135

Suzette: (Illustration 394) $25-35

Tinyteen: (Illustration 383) $100-120 (mint-in-box)

Tinyteen (or Suzette) and Bob: (Illustration 382) $35-45 each (higher for unusual outfit)

Vermont Maid®: (Illustration 396) $35-45

UNIQUE DOLL COMPANY

Ellie May Clampett: (Illustration 398) $30-35

High-Heeled Teen: (Illustration 397) $20-30

UNKNOWN

Bride: (Illustration 404) $50-60

Cloth Wardrobe for Boy Dolls: (Illustration 401) $10-15

Coat Doll: (Illustration 402) $85-95

Girl in Pink Print Dress: (Illustration 399) $15-20

Girl in Playsuit: (Illustration 403) $85-95

Laurie: (Illustration 405); doll $40-50; boxed outfits $15-20

Mary Lou — Doll Mannequin: (Illustration 400) $25

Teen Boy: (Illustration 406) $30

VALENTINE DOLLS, INC.

Perfect Patient: (Illustration 407) $50-85 (mint-in-box)

Queen for a Day: (Illustration 409) $80-110

VIRGA COMPANY

Doll in Lounging Clothes: (Illustration 411) $85-100

Go-Go by Schiaparelli: (Illustration 412); doll $125-140 (mint-in-box; higher prices have been paid for unusual dolls); outfit $30-40 (mint-in-box; depending on type)

VOGUE DOLLS, INC.

Brikette: (Illustration 422) $90-110

Brikette and Li'l Imp: (Illustrations 423 and 424) $90-125

Ginny: doll alone; no *Ginny* $125-150

Jan: (Illustration 421) $50-75

Jan and Jeff: (Illustration 418); *Jeff* $80-90; *Jan* $75-90

Jeff: (Illustration 414) $60-80

Jeff: (Illustration 415); doll in box $100-130; boxed outfit $35-50

Jill and Jan: (Illustraton 417); *Jill* $100-140 (depending on costume); *Jan* $75-90 (depending on costume)

Littlest Angel: (Illustration 427, two dolls in center) $35-45

Littlest Angel: (Illustration 427, left and right) $35-45

Love Me Linda: (Illustration 426) $65-75 (all original)

Wee Imp: (Illustration 425); doll boxed with brochure $200-220

OTHER BOOKS BY THE AUTHORS

Cloth Dolls Identification & Price Guide: 1920s and 1930s
Expansive photo guide to cloth dolls made by Lenci, Nora Welling, Chad Valley and many others. Lavishly illustrated with a bevy of beautiful photos plus packed with detailed descriptions to make identification simple. Loaded with 1990 values by the best selling author of the **Hard Plastic Doll** series. Features 47 color and 271 b/w photographs. 256 pages. 5½" x 8". PB. Item #H3979. $12.95

Compo Dolls 1928-1955 Identification and Price Guide
A long-awaited, much needed guide to composition dolls aids collectors with those favorite postwar friends. 428 photographs with 130 in color, display difficult-to-identify dolls augmented by a bevy of 208 pages of detailed text contain the most-up-to-date accurate values. An indispensable book for modern doll collectors! 208 pages. 8½" x 11". HB. Item #H4389. $25.00

Hard Plastic Dolls, Vol. 1., 3rd Revised Edition
An indispensable identification and price guide for every collector wanting to know more about hard plastic dolls of the 40s and 50s and their collectors values. 304 pages. 5½" x 8". PB. #H4638. $14.95

Hard Plastic Dolls, Vol. II
Second volume of a multitude of additional hard plastic dolls with identification and values. More than 43 color and 394 b/w photos aid the collector in studying and valuing their dolls. Organized both by type of doll and their manufacturer, this is a deluxe easy-to-use reference book. 256 pages. 5½" x 8". PB. Item #H3823. $12.95

**Santa Dolls & Figurines Price Guide:
Antique to Contemporary**
Discover valuable information about your favorite Santa collectibles from the information and price guide as well as the legends of Gift-Givers from other countries. Enjoy the different styles of Santa dolls, figurines, paper dolls and postcards and their costumes in 121 gorgeous color photographs and 146 b/w photographs. 160 pages. 5½" x 8". PB. Item #H4412. $14.95